Canadian
Lifesaving Manual

With the 2010 CPR guidelines.

LIFESAVING SOCIETY
The Lifeguarding Experts

Foreword

The Lifesaving Society is dedicated to preventing drowning and other water-related deaths and injuries. To achieve this, the Society develops products, programs, and services that will help people enjoy water activities safely.

This manual, *The Canadian Lifesaving Manual* (*CLSM*), is one of those products. And the courses it's used in — Bronze Medallion, for example — are just some of the programs the Society has developed to prevent drowning and other water-related deaths and injuries in Canada. This manual reflects current knowledge about suggested or preferred methods of lifesaving.

Countless individuals have contributed to the writing, editing, technical review, and production of this manual. Among them are both volunteers and staff of the Society and numerous individuals outside the Society who gave generously of their time and talents. The Society would like to extend special thanks to the following:

The Society staff, who provided invaluable assistance throughout the project. Particular thanks to Catherine Haza and Susan Casey for facilitating the project through the national office.
- ❑ the CLSM contract staff —
  - Shelley Henderson, for her good-natured coaching of Society staff, contract staff, and the Editorial Board. As project manager, Shelley provided the helpful, resourceful guidance so necessary in a project of this magnitude.
  - Richard Huint, for his efforts in the early days of the project.
  - Matra.gs, for their commitment and attention to the translation into French.
  - Ari Niemi, for his skill and dedication in the production of countless illustrations.
  - Louise Wood, for her tireless dedication to "getting it right." Her combination of strong opinions and willingness to work as a teammate made the editorial experience a most positive encounter for the Editorial Board.

❏ technical experts. Many were consulted to ensure the technical accuracy and completeness of *The Canadian Lifesaving Manual*. A special thanks for their assistance on the topic of hypothermia to Gordon Giesbrecht, Ph.D., University of Manitoba; Ron Golling, Kelowna Fire Department; and Rod-Paul Martin, British Columbia & Yukon Branch. Also, thanks to Steve B. Beerman, B.Sc., BSR, MD, CCFP, for his technical review of material on near-drowning and first aid.

❏ The many Lifesaving Society Branches that responded generously with feedback. In particular, thanks go to the Alberta & Northwest Territories Branch and Ontario Branch for their detailed, helpful guidance.

❏ The Society's Quebec Branch, for co-ordinating the review of the French translation.

❏ The Editorial Board, which guided the manual from rough draft through several rewritings and editings —

- Barney Chanda, for his overall insight and direction. Thanks too, for writing the draft of Chapter 8 and for providing assistance on Chapter 9.

- Phil Fournier and the members of his Saskatchewan writing team, for paying consistent attention to detail and contributing significantly to the drafting of Chapters 4, 5, and 8.

- Sue Glover Takahashi, for her stewardship as Chair of the Editorial Board. Her talent in both project management and writing — especially on Chapters 3, 4, 5, 8, 9, and 10 — were critical to the completion of *The Canadian Lifesaving Manual*.

- Anne Jackson, for her thoughtful, reflective approach and her guidance in the drafting of Chapters 1, 2, 4, and 5.

- members Calum MacLeod, Alphonse Montminy, and Sue Stewart-Greene, for guiding and directing the early "parts" of the project.

- Ed Madill, for his consistently incisive and witty contributions. Without losing sight of "the grand design," Ed never failed to find missing commas or misspelled words. He also wrote drafts of Chapters 4, 6, and 9 and provided materials for Chapters 3 and 5.

The Lifesaving Society believes that *The Canadian Lifesaving Manual* will continue to play an important role in the prevention of drowning and other water-related deaths and injuries for many years to come. Lifesavers in Canada will learn from this manual, teach from it, and — ultimately — contribute to it.

How to Use This Manual

Welcome to the world of lifesaving! This manual, *The Canadian Lifesaving Manual* (CLSM), will be used in lifesaving and lifeguarding courses offered by the Lifesaving Society. Lifesaving skills focus on preventing water-related injuries and saving lives. Participants of all ages and abilities can be included in lifesaving.

The Canadian Lifesaving Manual presents up-to-date information on how to be a lifesaver. The manual focuses on key steps, and it describes the most common techniques. To become an effective lifesaver, you need to *learn* this material and *adapt* it: to the situation, to the person you're rescuing, and to yourself as a rescuer.

We've tried to make this manual as practical and easy to use as possible. We've included lots of special notes and tips, and there are over 350 illustrations. There's also an index, which you can use to quickly find information on specific topics.

Each chapter in the manual provides *knowledge* that's vital to rescues. This knowledge will help you develop your *judgment* in rescues. Practising specific techniques will help you refine the *skill* needed in rescues. When you add personal *fitness*, you have it *all* — the four components of water rescue!

The manual has 10 chapters and three appendices:
- ❏ Chapter 1 — Be a Hero: You Can Make a Difference!
- ❏ Chapter 2 — Drowning Prevention
- ❏ Chapter 3 — Self-rescue
- ❏ Chapter 4 — The Rescue of Others
- ❏ Chapter 5 — Specialized Lifesaving Skills
- ❏ Chapter 6 — First Aid: The Rescue Process
- ❏ Chapter 7 — Lifesaving Priorities: The ABCs
- ❏ Chapter 8 — First Aid: The Treatment of Illness or Injury
- ❏ Chapter 9 — Rescue Strokes and Skills
- ❏ Chapter 10 — Physical Fitness and Lifesaving
- ❏ Appendix A — Stress Reactions to Rescues
- ❏ Appendix B — The Society's Policy Guidelines on Rescue Breathing Practice
- ❏ Appendix C — Swimming Principles.

We hope you enjoy and benefit from *The Canadian Lifesaving Manual*.

Contents

Contents

Chapter 1
Be a Hero:
You Can Make a Difference!

1.1   Introduction

As a lifesaver, *you can make a difference*. You can help other people or even save them from drowning, and you can be very influential in helping others be Water Smart in, on, and around water.

This chapter presents key facts on drownings in Canada. It shows what behavior increases risk and what behavior reduces risk in, on, and around water, and it describes how *you* can make a difference in drownings in Canada.

When you help someone else or save someone from drowning, you are being a hero. In lifesaving, being a hero means having the training to be a hero, and it means staying safe as you do this. It is NOT about risking your life to save others!

There are many ways to be a hero, and several stories about real-life rescues in Canada are included in this chapter. In each of the stories presented, the rescuer exercised *judgment*, put lifesaving *knowledge* into practice, showed *skill*, and demonstrated *fitness*. Can you see these in the stories?

The training programs of the Royal Life Saving Society Canada ("the Society") focus on these four components of a successful rescue. The techniques presented in this manual and in the lifesaving programs of the Society will help you make a difference.

If every lifesaver influences just one family member or friend, change can occur and lives can be saved! Canada needs more heroes. You can be one too!!

1.2   Drowning: Some Facts

The Society is dedicated to saving lives through drowning prevention. Since 1991, the Society has conducted research on all drownings and water-related deaths in all Canadian provinces and territories. This research provides the facts on the drowning "problem," and these facts are used to help the Society and others develop drowning-prevention "solutions." The Society's drowning research is the basis of its public-education campaigns, and it plays a major role in the development and refinement of the Society's lifesaving, lifeguarding, and leadership programs.

This research tells us a lot about drowning and fatal aquatic incidents in Canada, for example, who the victims are, where and when drownings occur, and what factors contribute to drowning. The rest of this section highlights these and other key facts on drowning in Canada.

How Serious Is the Drowning Problem?
❏ About 500 Canadians die each year in water-related incidents, and most of these deaths are preventable.
❏ Drowning is the third leading cause of all accidental deaths in Canada, exceeded only by motor vehicle collisions and falls.
❏ Among children under 10, drowning is the second leading cause of accidental death.
❏ More people die from drowning tha n from fires or poisonings in Canada.
❏ Drowning is the leading cause of death in recreational activities.
❏ Drownings can result in severe emotional and financial crises.

Who Drowns?
❏ *No one* is immune to drowning. People in all age groups, from the very young to the very old, die in water-related incidents.
❏ The age groups at greatest risk of drowning are
  ● young adults 18 to 34
  ● young children under 5.

> **Rescue from Ice**
> On Sunday, January 13, 1993, 9-year-old Jordan McMullan, dressed in full hockey equipment, skated onto thin ice chasing a puck and broke through the frozen surface of Mill Pond in Strathroy, Ontario. His friend, Christopher Siddall, 13 years of age, went to his aid, lay down on the ice which was cracking around him, and pulled Jordan to safety using his hockey stick.

BE WATER SMART.
PARENTS! LIFEGUARDS DON'T SUPERVISE BATHTUBS. YOU DO.

 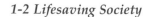

❏ Males are far more likely to drown than females. About four out of every five people who drown in Canada are male.

❏ Swimmers and non-swimmers drown. Knowing how to swim is *not* enough to protect against drowning.

What Activities Are Involved?

❏ About two-thirds of the people who drown are near the water but do *not* intend to go in.

❏ Two-thirds of water-related deaths occur during recreational activities in, on, or near the water. Fishing, powerboating, and swimming are the leading activities involved in water-related deaths occurring during recreational activity. Other significant activities are playing or walking near water, canoeing, and snowmobiling.

❏ About 50 people drown every year in bathtubs.

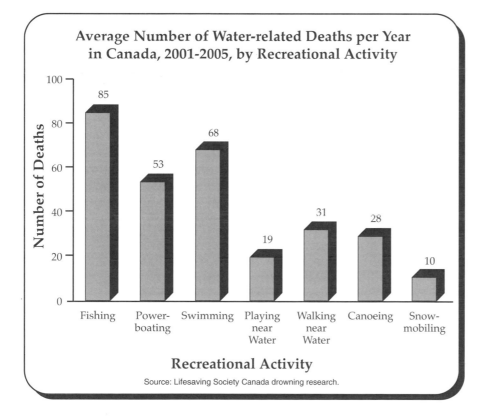

Average Number of Water-related Deaths per Year in Canada, 2001-2005, by Recreational Activity

Source: Lifesaving Society Canada drowning research.

City Boy Saved from Drowning

By Peter Smith and Kevin Martin

Calgary Sun

CALGARY — Two Calgary lifeguards saved a young boy's life yesterday. Matthew Brown, 7, of northeast Calgary, had been taking swimming lessons with a day-care group. "After their lessons had finished, they had a spell of free swimming time, and the boy was seen on the bottom in 1° metres of water," said Const. Larry Lafreniere.

Ken Schaffer, of the Emergency Medical Services, said the boy wasn't breathing when he was taken from the water. "By the time paramedics arrived, the boy was conscious, alert and was doing well," said Schaffer. "We would like to give a pat on the back to the lifeguards for a job well done. Their promptness and professional care saved a young life."

When Do Drownings Occur?

❏ Canadian drownings usually peak in the summer. While about half of all drownings happen in June, July, and August, *drownings are a year-round problem*.

❏ Many drownings and water-related deaths occur on the weekend, when participation in aquatic recreation is highest.

❏ Two-thirds of all drownings occur in the afternoon and evening.

Where Do Drownings Happen?

❑ Drowning rates are highest in the coastal provinces.

❑ Almost all drownings in Canada happen in unsupervised areas (without lifeguards).

❑ About three-quarters of the drownings in Canada happen at lakes, rivers, streams, and oceans. Very few occur at supervised pools.

What Are the Contributing Factors?

❑ About 90% of drowning victims are not wearing a lifejacket or PFD. Fewer than 3% of boating victims are wearing one, and a surprising proportion do not have one in their boat.

❑ Alcoholic beverages are a factor in almost half of all drownings.

❑ In almost half of all drownings, the victim is alone. There is *no chance* for a buddy to help.

❑ Cold water is an important factor in drownings. Nearly three-quarters of all deaths from exposure involve cold water.

Profiles of Some Typical Drowning Victims

Unattended Toddlers
Children under 5 who are playing near the water or bathing can fall into the water or submerge and drown if left unattended, even for a very short time.

Young Explorers
These are children between 5 and 12 who are playing near lakes, rivers, streams, and private pools, often without adult supervision.

Risk Takers
These are males aged 18 to 34 who powerboat, fish, swim, canoe, and snowmobile. Risk takers often party with friends, drinking alcohol and wearing neither a lifejacket nor a PFD.

Older, Not Wiser
These are males 35 to 64 who powerboat, fish, swim, and walk near water. They often drink during these activities, especially on open water.

Unsuspecting Seniors
These include males and females over 65. They are often alone when they drown, and they are at risk while walking near water or taking baths because they cannot rescue themselves.

Shallow-Water Divers
These are usually male teenagers, often drinking or partying, who dive into shallow water in backyard pools or at unsupervised waterfronts. They break their neck when they hit the bottom.

1.3   How to Make a Difference

Here are just some of the ways you can make a difference:
- ✓ Become aware of who's at risk. Do *you* fit one of the high-risk profiles? (See page 1-4.)
- ✓ Learn the keys to being Water Smart. Do *you* follow the Water Smart tips? (See page 2-2.)
- ✓ Get involved in drowning prevention by contacting your local pool, your Society Branch, or the Society national office.
- ✓ Become a trained lifesaver. The next section contains an overview of the Society, which is responsible for lifesaving training in Canada.

1.4   What Is the Royal Life Saving Society Canada?

The Lifesaving Society works to prevent drowning and water-related injury. The Society sets the standard for aquatic safety in Canada and certifies all of Canada's National Lifeguards.

Millions of Canadians hold Lifesaving Society certifications. Over 800,000 Canadians participate in the Society's training programs every year.

The Society is a national, volunteer organization and registered charity composed of tens of thousands of individual members and over 4,000 affiliated swimming pools, waterfronts, schools and clubs. The Lifesaving Society represents Canada internationally in the Commonwealth Royal Life Saving Society and the International Life Saving Federation.

House Commends Youth for Plucking Family from Death
By Craig Westcott
The Evening Telegram
ST. JOHN'S — There's a new hero in the province, a 13-year-old girl from Nain [Newfoundland] who saved three members of her family and a friend from drowning after their snowmobiles plunged through thin ocean ice.

Sherry Dicker was riding a snowmobile Sunday with her 11-year-old friend Shelly Dicker on the back when she saw the machine carrying her father, brother and sister slice through the ice ahead of her.

Dicker jumped off her snowmobile and hopped onto a safe pan of ice before [her snowmobile] also dropped into the water, carrying her friend with it. Dicker threw her coat to the girl and pulled her to safety.

With her father David, 38, brother David Jr., five, and her eight-year-old sister Stacy-Lee thrashing around in the water trying to keep afloat, Dicker crawled to the edge of the ice and again flung out her jacket and pulled each of them to safety.

Torngat Mountains MHA Garfield Warren asked the House of Assembly Tuesday to officially thank the Grade 8 student for being so brave. "The people of Nain are extremely pleased that they have an outstanding citizen that deserves credit and recognition for her heroic deeds," Warren said.

What Are the Aims and Values of the Society?

The *aims* of the Society are as follows:

❏ Prevention—to increase awareness of the responsibility that individuals assume for themselves and others when working, playing, or boating in, on, or near water

❏ Education—to provide education in response to current needs in water rescue, resuscitation, lifeguarding, and aquatic risk management

❏ Leadership—to provide leadership training and development for lifesaving and lifeguarding programs and activities.

The Society summarizes its *values* as follows:

✓ Humanitarian principles are the basis of the Society.
✓ People are the Society's most important resource.
✓ The Society is dynamic and action-oriented.
✓ The Society is based on mutual respect, trust, and integrity.
✓ The Society supports innovation and creativity.

How Does the Society Accomplish Its Aims?

The Society accomplishes its aims through

❏ program education
❏ public education
❏ research
❏ partnerships
❏ consultation.

Program Education

Program education refers to the formal training in swimming, lifesaving, lifeguarding and leadership provided by the Society. The Society reviews and revises its programs on a regular basis.

The programs of the Society are offered through the Society's affiliate members. Affiliate members include the pools and waterfronts of municipal recreation departments, local YMCA-YWCAs, youth camps, private programs, and the athletic facilities of schools, colleges, and universities. Over 800,000 Canadians are trained and certified every year in the Society's programs.

Public Education

Public education refers to the Society's efforts to ensure that all Canadians are "Water Smart." Being Water Smart involves acting safely near water and avoiding water-related hazards. The Society creates Water-Smart messages featuring personal lifesaving tips for people involved in unsupervised activities in, on, or near water. These messages are directed at Canadians who do *not* enrol in aquatic training programs. These people are not exposed to information on self-rescue and the prevention of aquatic accidents and may not know how to cope with aquatic emergencies involving others. The Society's public-education efforts reach millions of Canadians every year.

Research
Each year, the Society conducts research that profiles drownings and other water-related deaths in Canada. This research is presented in national drowning reports that identify the key factors contributing to these incidents. Education initiatives are developed from this research. The Society also holds symposiums on key lifesaving and public-education topics each year. In addition, the Society investigates issues that affect the development and technical excellence of its programs and services.

Partnerships
The Society works in co-operation and consultation with national, provincial, regional, and community agencies, governments, and organizations in the areas of prevention, education, safe boating, and aquatic safety.

Consultation
The Society provides advice to education, recreation, health, and government agencies that oversee aquatic recreation in Canada. In addition, Society representatives act as expert witnesses at coroner's inquests and in court cases.

How Can *You* Get Involved?
The Society has Branches, volunteers, and staff serving every province and territory in Canada.

At the national level, the Society is governed by a volunteer Board of Directors. The Board is responsible for policy development and strategic management of the Society. The Society's national office is in Ottawa.

> **Father and Son Rescued from Capsized Boat**
>
> Kim Richardson completed her Bronze Medallion course at Centennial Pool in Hope, British Columbia, on August 11, 1991. Six days later she found herself employing those skills she had learned when she was faced with a real life and death situation.
>
> She and her husband were camping on Gillis Lake. About 6:00 p.m. Kim heard a loud splash accompanied by an ear-piercing cry. Looking out onto the lake she saw a capsized boat with one person in the water and one hanging onto the craft.
>
> Kim's husband Bob went for help and Kim rowed her rubber dinghy out to the overturned boat. As she approached the victims, the father, who was beginning to submerge because of his heavy clothes, called desperately to his son. Suddenly, his son let go of the overturned boat and began to swim towards his drowning father. Both men began to submerge. Kim called to them, encouraging them to roll onto their backs.
>
> Using her paddle, Kim pulled the son to her boat and held onto him. Just then, a small motor boat arrived and helped the father.

At the provincial/territorial level, a Branch Council or Board of Directors directs the management of Society activities. There are 10 Branches, and all provinces and territories are represented by a Branch. Branch Councils consist of volunteers serving as Branch officers and committee chairpersons. Most Branches elect or appoint committee members, event co-ordinators, or area representatives to extend the work of their Council. All Branches have offices, and most have paid staff. Staff and volunteers work closely in pursuit of the aims of the Society.

Once you receive a Society program award, you become a "member" of the Society and are invited to participate in the activities of its provincial and territorial Branches. But you don't have to own a bathing suit to help save lives through drowning prevention. You can help in your local or provincial public-education or fund-raising campaigns.

The Society encourages you to get involved. There are many ways to be a hero!

How Does the Society Honor Heroes?

The Society acknowledges significant acts of bravery with its rescue awards:

The award for the most courageous rescue in the Commonwealth is called the Mountbatten Medal, and it is awarded by the Royal Life Saving Society. The Canadian nomination for the Mountbatten Medal is selected from annual recommendations for the M. G. Griffiths Plaque.

- ❏ *Letter of Commendation.* The letter of commendation acknowledges a successful rescue by a person who does *not* hold a Society award.
- ❏ *Rescue Commendation Certificate.* This certificate recognizes an outstanding rescue by a person who does *not* hold a Society award.
- ❏ *M. G. Griffiths Certificate* and *M. G. Griffiths Plaque.* These two awards acknowledge significant acts of bravery and the use of approved techniques by a person who holds a Society award in an attempt to save a life. The M. G. Griffiths Plaque is the highest Society rescue award.

Anyone may nominate a person for a Society rescue award. Recognition is primarily given for a lifesaving act in a volunteer capacity, but outstanding on-duty rescues are also eligible for consideration. Nominations for a rescue award should be submitted to the provincial or territorial Branch as soon as possible after the rescue.

The Society encourages you to nominate your local hero for a rescue award. Please contact your provincial or territorial Branch to find out how.

1.5 Want to Know More?

Royal Life Saving Society Canada. *Swim Patrol Award Guide* and *Bronze Medals Award Guide*. Ottawa: Royal Life Saving Society Canada, 2009.

> Award guides present the test items, evaluation criteria and teaching suggestions for the three awards in the Society's Canadian Swim Patrol Program - Rookie, Ranger and Star Patrol, and the three bronze medal awards - Bronze Star, Bronze Medallion and Bronze Cross.

Royal Life Saving Society Canada. *Program Guide*. Ottawa: Royal Life Saving Society Canada.

> The *Program Guide* is produced by individual Society Branches. It presents the details of Society programs and describes how to run them. This publication, which is of interest to aquatic programmers, covers Branch policies and administrative procedures.

Royal Life Saving Society Canada. The *National Drowning Report*, 2011 Edition. Ottawa: The Royal Life Saving Society Canada. May 2011.

> This report profiles the who, what, when, where and why of drowning trends in Canada since 1997.

Sportsmart Canada. *Sudden Impact*. Toronto: Sportsmart Canada, 1992.

> A 20-minute video on diving injuries, *Sudden Impact* focuses on the potential dangers of diving into both known and unknown water. The video has been produced for young people, and it features interviews with teenagers who have been seriously injured while diving. The video also stresses the role of alcohol in diving injuries and the dangers associated with diving in backyard pools.

Chapter 2
Drowning Prevention

2.1   Introduction

Being a lifesaver is of course about rescuing *others* from danger around water. But it's also about *drowning prevention* and *self-rescue*. These two topics are so important that each has its own chapter in this book. This chapter covers drowning prevention, and Chapter 3 discusses self-rescue.

Drowning prevention *matters*. Drowning is a leading cause of accidental death in Canada. In fact, it is the *third* leading cause of such death, with more fatalities every year than poisonings or even fires.

Many drownings and other serious aquatic incidents *can be prevented*. They are therefore not real "accidents." Research conducted by the Royal Life Saving Society Canada shows just how true this is. All too often, drownings happen because people take chances around water. In many cases, people would not have drowned if they had been *Water Smart* — if they'd worn a personal flotation device (PFD), for example.

This chapter presents specific tips on how to prevent drownings. By following these tips, you can decrease your chances of getting into trouble in, on, or near the water.

**Enter unknown water
feet first, first time**

The tips presented in this chapter are all drawn from the Society's research on drowning. To find out more about this research, see Chapter 1.

2.2 Be Water Smart—Prevent Drownings!

Here are some important Water-Smart tips to help *you* prevent drownings:
- ✓ Learn to swim.
- ✓ Wear a lifejacket or PFD.
- ✓ Behave responsibly if you consume alcohol, drugs, or medication.
- ✓ Behave responsibly when boating.
- ✓ Supervise toddlers and young children at all times.
- ✓ Swim with a Water-Smart buddy nearby.
- ✓ Don't dive into shallow or unknown water.
- ✓ Check for hazards, and create a safe aquatic setting.
- ✓ Swim in supervised areas.
- ✓ Know the dangers of cold water.
- ✓ Know the dangers of warm water.

Learn to Swim

Basic swimming ability is a fundamental requirement to effective drowning prevention. Everyone should learn to swim – at least to the Lifesaving Society's Canadian Swim to Survive® Standard.

And once you know how to swim,
- ❏ never swim alone
- ❏ swim parallel to shore
- ❏ have someone accompany you by boat if you plan to swim in open water
- ❏ be *realistic* about your strength and swimming ability.

Wear a Lifejacket or PFD

Wear a lifejacket whenever you are playing or working on or near water. This is *very* important, especially for boaters, toddlers, young children, and non-swimmers. Set an example for children, guests, and others—wear a lifejacket or PFD when you expect *them* to wear one.

Most people who drown weren't "swimming" when they drowned. Most weren't planning to be in the water. And most weren't wearing lifejackets or PFDs. Instead, they were on or near the water, and something unexpected happened.

Proper Fitting and Wearing of Lifejackets and PFDs
- ✓ Pick a lifejacket or PFD you like that suits each of your activities well. (You may need different lifejackets or PFDs for different activities.)
- ✓ Be sure any snaps, ties, or zippers work well.
- ✓ Make sure the lifejacket or PFD fits snugly but comfortably. Lift up your arms; if the lifejacket or PFD goes above your chin, it's too big.

Canadian Swim to Survive® Standard

Society research finds that over 70% of drowning victims do not plan to enter the water. And they don't have the essential skills required to survive an unepected fall into deep water: orient and support yourself at the surface after an unexpected entry, and swim to safety.

The following basic skills form the Canadian Swim to Survive® Standard:

- ✓ Roll into deep water
- ✓ Tread water 1 minute
- ✓ Swim 50 metres

Contact the Lifesaving Society or your local aquatic facility for information about Swim to Survive®.

✓ Make sure the lifejacket or PFD is easy to put on and take off.
✓ Check that your arms can move freely and you can bend at the waist without the top riding up in your face.
✓ Sit down with your lifejacket or PFD on. If it pushes up under your chin and you feel very uncomfortable, it's too big.
✓ A lifejacket or PFD for a child should have a strap between the legs and a collar with a grab handle.
✓ Test old lifejackets and PFDs for flotation — flotation material deteriorates over time.

Proper-fitting PFD

Behave Responsibly if You Consume Alcohol, Drugs, or Medication

If you consume alcohol, drugs, or medication, avoid activities requiring quick reaction times, fine motor skills, and judgment. For example, DON'T dive off a dock, DON'T go water skiing, and DON'T drive a boat. Because intoxication interferes with your ability to handle dangerous situations, it increases the chances that a drowning or severe accident will occur. If you are taking medication, ask your doctor how it could affect your ability to swim, drive, or react to stress.

Behave Responsibly when Boating

When going out in *any* boat,
✓ wear a lifejacket or PFD.
✓ obey boating regulations.
✓ make sure that mandatory and recommended safety equipment is on board. No matter how little storage space the boat has, make sure there is one lifejacket or PFD for each person. (See sidebar for some of the basic equipment required by law for many small boats.)
✓ know the boat's limits, especially those regarding stability and buoyancy.
✓ always check weather conditions before going out.
✓ watch the sky for changes, and head for safety if bad weather threatens.
✓ keep your weight low and centred—*never* stand up in small boats.
✓ stay away from swimming areas, rocks, strong currents, dams, and other boats.
✓ always tell someone where you're going and when you think you'll be back.

> ### Required Equipment for Many Small Boats
>
> ✓ 1 Canadian-approved PFD or lifejacket of appropriate size for each person on board
> ✓ Buoyant heaving line at least 15 m long
> ✓ Manual propelling device (e.g., paddles, oars) or an anchor with at least 15 m of cable, rope or chain
> ✓ Bailer or manual water pump
> ✓ Watertight flashlight or 3 Canadian-approved flares
> ✓ Sound signalling device (e.g., whistle, horn)
>
> *Required equipment varies with the size and type of boat. For details, refer to Lifesaving Society BOAT Study Guide or the latest edition of Transport Canada's Safe Boating Guide.*

✓ always dress warmly enough to protect against losing body heat — if you get too cold, you won't be able to operate your boat. Dress appropriately, and wear such added protection as waterproof boots or shoes, a warm hat or toque, and gloves.

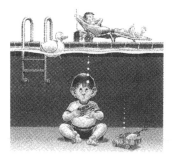

BE WATER SMART.
TODDLERS REQUIRE ADULT SUPERVISION.

Supervise Toddlers and Young Children at All Times

Never leave toddlers and young children alone near water. They can slip underwater and drown even if they're alone for *an instant*.

Be especially careful in the home—toddlers and young children can drown in the bathtub even if you leave the room for just a moment.

Swim with a Water-Smart Buddy Nearby

People of any age or swimming ability can find themselves in trouble in the water. This is why it's so important to swim with a Water-Smart buddy—there's someone there to help.

Don't Dive into Shallow or Unknown Water

Always enter unknown or shallow water *feet first, first time.* Diving into unknown or shallow water shatters lives. Don't do it—you could drown or be totally paralyzed.

HOW DO YOU FIT A 5½ FOOT DIVER IN A 4½ FOOT SPACE?

YOU DON'T.
ALWAYS CHECK THE DEPTH.
FEET FIRST, FIRST TIME.

NEVER dive into unknown or shallow water, and NEVER push anyone into the water!!

Check for Hazards, and Create a Safe Aquatic Setting

Checking for hazards and creating a safe aquatic setting are key parts of preventing drownings. Page 2-5 presents detailed tips on these aspects of drowning prevention.

Check for underwater hazards

Swim in Supervised Areas

Whenever possible, swim in areas supervised by qualified lifeguards. At such locations, staff plan, supervise, and control activities, and lifeguards provide help when it's needed.

Checking for Hazards and Creating a Safe Aquatic Setting

Streams, Rivers, Ponds, Lakes, and Oceans

✓ Check for currents *before* entering the water, and assess their strength.
✓ Before swimming, check for and note any sandbanks, weeds, rocks, tree branches, or other underwater hazards.
✓ Before swimming, check whether the bottom is uneven or soft. With underwater drop-offs and holes, you can suddenly find yourself in deeper water. It's a good idea to use a pole and wear shoes.
✓ Be cautious the first time you swim where there's a current.
✓ Before walking near the water's edge, check for slippery surfaces, loose rocks, soft shoulders, etc.
✓ Avoid overhanging banks — they can give way suddenly.
✓ When swimming, be aware of and avoid nearby boats.
✓ To avoid drifting too far from the swimming area, choose and refer regularly to a specific landmark.
✓ Watch for and avoid water toys (surfboards, balls, etc.). They can be hazardous *even when abandoned.*
✓ Never rely on inflatable cushions, air mattresses, water toys, etc., for the support of non-swimmers.

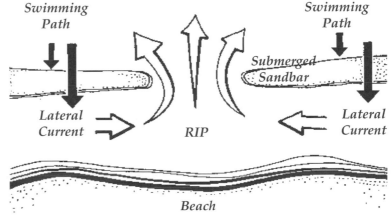

Swimming path across current

Supervised Pools, Waterparks, and Waterfronts

✓ Read and abide by all rules and instructions.
✓ Co-operate with those in charge (lifeguards, supervisors, etc.) — they're there to keep the area safe for you and others.
✓ Take responsibility for your own safety — don't assume lifeguards or others can do it all for you.
✓ Ensure that toddlers and young children are supervised at close range.
✓ Check any depth markings to determine which areas are shallow and deep and where drop-off or transition zones are.
✓ Stay out of deep water unless you can swim well.
✓ Always WALK on pool decks, in shower or locker rooms, or on docks.

Unsupervised Pools and Waterfronts

Do as for supervised pools, waterparks, and waterfronts, but add the following:
✓ Make sure there's a phone right at the water's edge — that way, you can answer the phone and *keep supervising activity.* Keep the phone line open in case there's an emergency.
✓ Post emergency numbers near the phone.
✓ Have rescue equipment and a first aid kit.
✓ Never let anyone swim alone.
✓ Avoid diving in backyard pools — they rarely have the depth or distance required for safe diving.
✓ Secure access to pool areas from both yard and home — it prevents small children from entering when they shouldn't. Install a fence *and* a locking gate.
✓ Use unbreakable containers near the water.

Know the Dangers of Cold Water

Always wear a lifejacket or PFD in conditions where the water *feels* cold to you. The longer you are in cold water, the greater the risk of death. (In fact, prolonged exposure to water *that does not feel cold at the start* can be dangerous and may lead to drowning.) And the colder the water, the faster unconsciousness and drowning occur. Cold water is dangerous even for excellent swimmers, because it reduces endurance, impairs judgment, and causes muscle cramps.

Falling into cold water from ice can be deadly. Driving or snowmobiling on ice can of course be extremely dangerous, but so can just walking on it. This is why it's so important to know the facts about ice.

> ### So What Do You Mean by Cold Water?
> Many factors affect how your body responds to cold water. Here are some of them:
> - ❏ length of time in the water
> - ❏ water temperature
> - ❏ amount of body fat
> - ❏ amount of the body that is submerged
> - ❏ whether clothing or a lifejacket is worn
> - ❏ body position
> - ❏ age.
>
> Water temperatures as warm as 20° Celsius are considered a risk for hypothermia (a dropping of the body's core temperature). For information on the treatment of this condition, see page 8-24.

Some Facts about Ice

- ❏ Ice seldom freezes or thaws at a uniform rate. It can be 30 centimetres thick in one spot but only 2 centimetres thick a few metres away. So before heading onto ice, check with someone who knows about local conditions, thin-ice areas, or dangerous open-water conditions.
- ❏ Ice in cities and towns is usually weaker than ice in rural areas. (This is because of the greater temperature changes in urban areas and the salt from nearby roads.)
- ❏ Ice in towns and cities often involves more water movement—and therefore more danger.

BE WATER SMART.
SNOWMOBILES ARE DEAD WEIGHT ON ICE.

Know the Dangers of Warm Water

The warm water in bathtubs, home spas, and public hot tubs can be dangerous. You can be overcome by the heat, and you can lose consciousness. In the water, this can lead to drowning.

Warm-water spas and hot tubs (40° Celsius) are not recommended for those with heart or circulatory problems, the very young, the elderly, and pregnant women. Do NOT use these facilities if you have any open sores or infections. And if you are receiving medical treatment, consult your doctor about the use of warm-water spas and tubs.

Here are some tips on how to avoid getting into trouble in warm water:

✓ Stay in warm water for less than 15 minutes.
✓ *Always* have someone nearby who can help in an emergency—*never* use a spa or hot tub alone.
✓ Consult your doctor if you're unsure about using warm-water spas and tubs.

2.3   Want to Know More?

Royal Life Saving Society Canada. *BOAT Study Guide*, Ninth Printing, Revised, March 2011. Royal Life Saving Society Canada, 1999.

> The 80-page, full colour *BOAT Study Guide* is the required reference for those taking the Society's Boat Operator Accredited Training course. It presents all the information required to earn the Pleasure Craft Operator (PCO) card.

Royal Life Saving Society Canada. The *National Drowning Report*, 2011 Edition. Ottawa: The Royal Life Saving Society Canada. May 2011.

> This report profiles the who, what, when, where and why of drowning trends in Canada since 1997.

Sportsmart Canada. *Sudden Impact*. Toronto: Sportsmart Canada, 1992.

> A 20-minute video on diving injuries, *Sudden Impact* focuses on the potential dangers of diving into both known and unknown water. The video has been produced for young people, and it features interviews with teenagers who have been seriously injured while diving. The video also stresses the role of alcohol in diving injuries and the dangers associated with diving in backyard pools.

Transport Canada. *Safe Boating Guide*. Ottawa: Ministry of Transport, 2009.

> This booklet provides up-to-date information on Canadian safe boating practices and on laws affecting watercraft in Canada. The guide is one of many tools the Office of Boating Safety uses to help educate recreational boaters about safety. See also www.boatingsafety.gc.ca.

Pleasure Craft Operator Card

Under federal regulations introduced in 1999, Canadian recreational boaters require a Pleasure Craft Operator Card (PCO card) to drive a boat powered by a motor. As of 2009, every recreational power-boat operator, regardless of age or size of craft, requires the PCO card.

Age & Horsepower Restrictions

Regulations matching boat power with capability and maturity are also now in effect. Youth under 16 years may not operate boats above certain power limits unless accompanied in the boat and directly supervised by someone 16 years or older.

Age	Max. power restriction
Under 12 years	10 hp (unaccompanied)
12 - 16 years	40 hp (unaccompanied)

Nobody under 16 years may operate personal watercraft (e.g., Sea-Doos, WaveRunners, Jet Skis) accompanied or not.

Chapter 3
Self-rescue

3.1   Introduction

Chapter 2 discussed how to be Water Smart and *prevent* aquatic accidents. But even the best prevention is not always enough. Despite taking Water-Smart precautions, you might someday get into trouble in, on, or around the water. For example, the canoe you are in might capsize if the water suddenly becomes very rough. Or you might slip and fall from a dock when you're alone.

Self-rescue: You never know when you'll be put to the test!

Self-rescue refers to the steps you take to get yourself out of these and other difficulties in, on, or near water. It's normal to feel surprised, confused, or afraid in such situations. But there is a basic process to use in any rescue situation, including self-rescue. And there are self-rescue skills you can learn for dealing with specific situations — falling into cold water, for instance. This chapter covers the following aspects of self-rescue:

❑ self-rescue: the rescue process — the basic process to use in *any* self-rescue situation
❑ self-rescue skills — instructions on how to handle *specific* self-rescue situations
❑ follow-up and evaluation — a summary of what to do once you're out of danger.

Once you've mastered these steps to self-rescue, you'll be ready to learn how to rescue others. That topic is covered in Chapter 4.

> Having strong swimming skills can help you handle dangerous situations in, on, and around the water (see Chapter 2, page 2-2). Experienced swimmers also develop good judgment about what situations in, on, or near water are dangerous.

3.2　Self-rescue: The Rescue Process

Whether you're rescuing yourself or another person, your rescue will have the same three elements. *In any self-rescue,* you must
✓ recognize
✓ assess
✓ act.

The rescue process applies to all self-rescue, and it's dynamic. You repeat the three elements again and again until you're out of the water, and you go through them again once you're out of the water. In some cases, you may recognize-assess-act many times, changing the procedures you choose as conditions change. It all depends on the rescue situation.

The rescue process is used in self-rescue, the rescue of others, and first aid. The three elements are the same in every type of rescue or first aid situation, but the element *details* are different. See Chapter 4 for how the process applies to the rescue of others, Chapter 6 for how it applies to first aid.

The rest of this section describes the elements in the rescue process as they apply to self-rescue.

Recognize
✓ *Recognize* that you are in trouble and that you must rescue yourself.
✓ *Recognize* that aspects of the situation, such as your condition, water conditions, and weather conditions, may be changing.

Assess
✓ What self-rescue skills do you (and those with you) have?
✓ What is your physical condition? Are you injured? Which of your injuries are the most important? How fit are you?
✓ Where is the closest point of safety?
✓ What are the water and weather conditions? How will they affect your options?
✓ What equipment do you have that might be useful in a self-rescue?
✓ What is the lowest-risk way of rescuing yourself?
✓ Are there bystanders? How can they help?

Act
✓ Do the things you decided to do in your assessment.
✓ Watch for changes that make reassessment necessary.
✓ Direct bystanders as needed.
✓ Contact the Emergency Medical System (EMS) if you need it. (See page 3-3.)
✓ Contact the authorities if the incident should be reported.

> **What's EMS?**
> The Emergency Medical System (EMS) is a community-wide system for responding to emergencies. It consists of police, fire, and ambulance services. To find these numbers in your community, check the front pages of the telephone book.

Calling EMS

After removing the victim from the water, direct him or her to a suitable location. Ask if the victim has friends or family he or she would like to call. If the victim is unconscious, ask if anyone knows the victim. Shout this if you have to!

Provide first aid and medical assistance if necessary (see Chapters 6, 7, and 8 for information on first aid). Be on the alert for indications of shock that might not have been clear earlier.

In contacting EMS, you need to give or get the following information:

- ❏ *who* you are and who the victim is
- ❏ *what* the victim's condition is
- ❏ *where* you are
- ❏ *how* the accident happened
- ❏ *when* EMS will arrive.

How you call EMS depends on where you are:

- ❏ Many communities use the 911 emergency telephone number, which connects the caller to an operator. The operator directs the call to any of the emergency-response services: ambulance, police, fire department, and so on. After the call has been transferred, a trained dispatcher leads the conversation and asks questions to obtain the required information.
- ❏ In communities not served by a 911 system, a separate telephone number is usually used for each emergency-response service. If you don't know the number, dial 0, and ask the operator for help.
- ❏ When calling from a public telephone, you don't need money to call EMS. Information on how to make an emergency call is often posted on the telephone itself.

After calling EMS, give a responsible person the job of meeting it and directing the emergency-response team to the victim. If you're alone, give EMS *detailed instructions* about your location.

When the EMS team arrives, *the team* assumes responsibility for the care of the victim. In some cases, emergency-response teams won't assume responsibility for the victim of an aquatic accident until he or she has been removed from the water. Offer help as needed, and provide information as you are asked for it (EMS teams follow their own action plans, and they ask for information as it is needed).

Reporting the Incident

When an incident occurs in an area where there is a relevant authority (provincial or territorial park authorities, lifeguards) or where additional assistance may be required (for example, from an electrical utility for the removal of electrical hazards), you may need to contact the relevant authority about the incident. Also, write things down while they're still fresh in your mind — how many witnesses there were, what the conditions were, what happened, etc. When doing this, refer to the guidelines and questions in Sections 6.4, 6.5, and 6.6 — they're a helpful framework for incident reports.

3.3   Self-rescue Skills

This section provides information that will help you *assess* and *act* in specific self-rescue situations:
- ❏ self-rescue from good water conditions
- ❏ self-rescue from cold water
- ❏ self-rescue from hot water
- ❏ self-rescue from moving water.

> To survive falling into water, non-swimmers should wear a lifejacket or PFD whenever they are near water. Many non-swimmers who drowned did NOT expect to have to swim (they were fishing, for example, and their boat overturned).

"Warm" water temperatures

Self-rescue from Good Water Conditions

The elements presented in Section 3.2 are an excellent *general* guide to self-rescue from good water conditions. But there are some *specific* conditions and factors you also need to consider:

✓ If the water is deep, move to safety if you can. If you *cannot*, call or signal for help as soon as you can. In the meantime, swim, tread water, or do a motionless float to keep yourself at the surface (see pages 3-6 and 3-7). Here are some pointers on when to use each of these three self-rescue skills:
- ● Consider swimming if no one can respond to your call for help within a few minutes. Swimming is a reasonable choice if you are in *known* water and the distance you need to swim is appropriate for your swimming skills, your energy level, and the environmental conditions.
- ● Treading water may result in less heat loss than motionless floating on the back (see below). But treading water may also take more effort than motionless floating.
- ● Any motionless position maintained at the surface of the water while breathing is called a *motionless float*. This self-rescue skill is useful whenever you have to conserve energy while waiting for help or resting. Motionless floating can be a useful survival skill in calm, warm water (water whose temperature is more than 20° Celsius). *Motionless floating is not recommended for self-rescue in cold water* (water whose temperature is 20° Celsius or less), because the head is a high heat-loss area, and placing it in water may increase the rate of heat loss and reduce core body temperature (the temperature of the internal organs).

✓ If your boat swamps or capsizes, think carefully about whether to stay with the overturned boat or swim to safety. Here are some points to consider:
- ● In general, stay with your boat, and wait to be rescued.
- ● Try to right your boat.
- ● *Always* right canoes, and use them as rescue craft. (You can use your hands to slowly paddle a swamped canoe to shore.)
- ● If help will probably *not* come, consider trying to reach shore safely while conserving as much energy as possible.

- Before deciding to swim to safety, carefully consider its pros and cons. See below for information on using swimming as a self-rescue skill.

✓ If your clothing is weighing you down, take steps to remove it. But NEVER take your clothes off if you're wearing a PFD, and remove clothing in cold water *only if wearing it threatens your survival*. When removing clothing in the water,

- remove one clothing item at a time. Make sure you get enough breath between each item removal — you can sink while removing heavy clothes.
- remove boots or shoes first.
- save lighter items for use in self-rescue or in the rescue of others.

✓ If you get into difficulty while sailboarding, remember that signalling distress is not as easy as with other such craft. Waving the arms in an exaggerated motion is one way to attract attention. So is setting off pocket-sized flares. Furl the sail, and place the mast and sail on the board as a distress signal. Either paddle to shore, or wait to be rescued.

> ### Using Clothing as a Self-rescue Assist
> While PFDs or lifejackets are much more effective, some clothing items make useful self-rescue assists or towing assists.
>
> ### Pants as Self-rescue Assists
> ✓ Tie a knot in each leg of the pants, close to the cuffs. Fasten the waist and the fly.
> ✓ Hold the pants in front of you with one hand with the waist open toward you. With your other hand, splash water into the waist of the pants. The pants fill with air from the splashing.
> ✓ When the pants are "full," close their waistband. The wet fabric will slow the passage of air through the material, making the pants buoyant. You can then use them as an assist.
>
> ### Shirts as Self-rescue Assists
> ✓ If it isn't too heavy or the water is cold, you may decide to keep your shirt on. Button the shirt at the cuffs and up the front. Tuck or tie the shirt at your waist.
> ✓ Exhale through your mouth into the neck opening of the shirt. The shirt fills with air. When the shirt is "full," button the shirt at the neck. The wet fabric will slow the passage of air through the material, making the shirt buoyant.

> ### Removing Clothing in Self-rescue
> ✓ Boots or shoes — get into a tuck position, and remove shoes one at a time.
> ✓ Jacket — in a back float position, use both hands to unfasten and remove the jacket.
> ✓ Pants — if necessary, unfasten the pants. You may do this while treading water legs only in a vertical position or while floating on your back. Then, in a tuck position, slide your pants off.
> ✓ Shirt — in either a back-float or a backward-leaning position, unfasten and remove the shirt.
> ✓ Pullover shirt or sweater — grasp the base of the shirt or sweater with crossed arms, and pull it over your head and arms in a single movement.
> ✓ Other clothes — there's no need to remove clothing that doesn't interfere with swimming movements.

Swimming

Here are some tips on using swimming as a self-rescue skill:

✓ If you have a watercraft or boat, decide if you will use it as a swimming assist.

✓ If there are currents, winds, or tides you can use to your advantage, consider them in planning your swimming route.

✓ If there is a buoyant object that will help keep you afloat, use it.

✓ PFDs or lifejackets make swimming a bit more difficult, but DON'T discard them.

✓ Swim with your head *up* unless you're in warm water.

✓ Don't swim too fast. Pace yourself, and keep your breathing relaxed and controlled. If you're in warm water or are wearing a PFD, you can rest if you feel fatigue in your muscles or breathing becomes difficult; otherwise, keep moving, but with reduced effort.

See Chapter 9 for detailed information on rescue strokes and skills.

Treading Water

You can use one of the following kicks when treading water. You may also alternate among these kicks to reduce fatigue:

Treading water with slow eggbeater kick

✓ *modified whip kick*. This is the most common choice in treading water. Instead of finishing the kick by bringing the legs together, make a wide and continuous rotary motion to give yourself more consistent support.

✓ *scissor kick*, modified so that the legs never fully close.

✓ *slow eggbeater kick*.

For arm action, use either a wide sculling action or a modified finning action. Technique for these leg and arm actions is presented in detail in Chapter 9.

Motionless Floating

In a motionless float, you need to find a position that keeps your nose and mouth *above* the water. You also need to keep your lungs as full as possible (this is especially important if you tend to sink easily). Hold your breath when you float motionless — blowing out makes you sink.

There are four kinds of motionless floats:

❏ *horizontal float*. Lie face up, horizontally, at the surface. For stability, either keep your arms straight and extended sideways OR extend them slightly backward and parallel. If you do the latter, keep your palms upward and just below the surface. The body rotates about the lungs. For optimal buoyancy, get into this position *gradually*, and *control* your breathing.

❏ *angled float*. If you have trouble with the horizontal float, you can use an angled float. Bend the knees, but keep the rest of the body in the position for the horizontal float. Again, the body rotates about the lungs.

❏ *vertical float*. "Stand" in deep water with your head tilted backward and all but your face submerged. You can use your arms to scull until you are motionless. Once motionless, drop your arms to your sides, or fold them below the surface and in front of your chest. Arch your back somewhat — it stabilizes the position.

❏ *front float*. In this variation of the vertical float, you hang motionless at the surface with your face in the water and hold your breath. By adjusting the position of your arms, you can find the best angle for this float. In preparation for a breath, exhale below the surface. As your mouth clears the surface to take a breath, press your arms downward *lightly* to help support your head. You can also use a scissor kick to help in this manoeuvre. Return to a resting position at the surface, with your face in the water, after taking a breath.

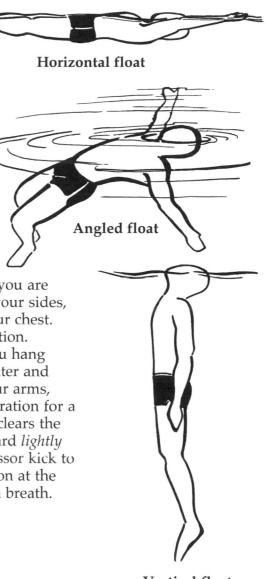

Horizontal float

Angled float

Vertical float

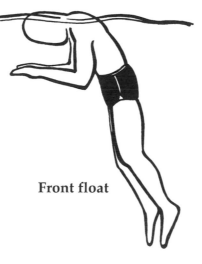

Front float

"Cold" water temperatures

Self-rescue from Cold Water

In self-rescue from cold water (see page 2-6), the priority is to get out of the water *fast*:
✓ Get out of the water, using a quick burst of energy to do so.
✓ Remove wet clothing immediately.
✓ Dry off and keep warm.

If you *cannot* do this, you must take appropriate action to extend your survival time while waiting to be rescued. Keep the following in mind while carrying out the elements in the rescue process:
✓ If you expect to be in the water for a long time, move *slowly* and *deliberately* to conserve heat. Expect a decrease in your strength *and* in your ability to move. Make the harder manoeuvres while you can.
✓ *While in the water*, keep your clothes on — it will help you conserve heat.
✓ If you aren't wearing a PFD or lifejacket, tread water (see page 3-6).
✓ If you are wearing a PFD or lifejacket, use one of the following strategies:

Heat Escape Lessening Position (HELP)

● The self-rescue skill of choice is HELP — the Heat Escape Lessening Position. Press your legs together, tuck them up, and press your arms against the sides of your chest. The head, sides of the chest, armpits, and groin are the body areas that lose the most heat. Using HELP limits heat loss because the head is out of the water, the tuck position protects the large blood vessels in the groin, and the arms cover the sides of the chest.

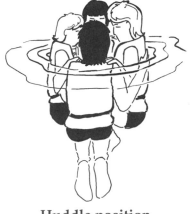

Huddle position

● Small groups of two to four can use the Huddle Position to reduce the rate of heat loss. People in the group should face one another, press their own legs together, press their chests

---

Immersion in Cold Water

Sudden immersion in cold water causes an immediate and large decrease in skin temperature. Several reflex "shock" responses occur:

❑ a gasp reflex, which causes a sudden breathing in, followed by uncontrolled, involuntary hyperventilation in which water may be breathed in

❑ a greatly reduced capacity to hold the breath

❑ an immediate and widespread constriction of blood vessels and an increase in heart rate and blood pressure.

Continued exposure to cold causes a rapid decline in strength and in the ability to use the fingers, hands, and limbs. It also becomes harder to hold onto rescue assists. The risks associated with sudden immersion in cold water are greatest when the body suffers a severe change of temperature, for example, on a hot day in early spring or late fall.

together, and interlock arms (one arm over and the other arm under a partner's). If the water is calm and currents aren't strong, it may be easier and more efficient to use HELP. But if these conditions are *not* present or there are children in the group, the Huddle Position is preferable (children in the middle). This position keeps the group together, and it can also boost morale.

✓ If you fall through ice, call for help. Use any combination of kicking, clawing, crawling, and breaking loose ice to find solid support. Move your feet and legs into a swimming position. Try to push yourself forward on your stomach onto the unbroken ice. DON'T stand up. Roll away from the break until you find solid ice.

✓ If you fell into cold water from a car or truck, try to escape while the vehicle is still floating. The most practical escape hatches are the windows; water and ice pressure make it very hard to open the doors of a submerging vehicle.

Ice self-rescue: Keeping low, push forward on your stomach

Self-rescue from Hot Water

The negative effects of hot water (water whose temperature is at least 40° Celsius, such as that in spas or hot tubs) include dizziness and weakness, which can affect balance. These effects don't usually appear until people stand up to get out of the water.

If you stand up in hot water and feel dizzy,
✓ get into a horizontal position
✓ crawl out of the water
✓ lie down on your side until you feel better
✓ call for help.

After *any* self-rescue from hot water, rest before starting your regular activities again. And drink water or other fluids before getting into hot water — it replaces fluids lost through sweating and so helps prevent negative effects.

"Hot" water: Limit your contact

Self-rescue from Moving Water

This section describes how to rescue yourself from
❑ undertows, rip currents, and lateral currents
❑ river and hydraulic currents.

Self-rescue from Undertows, Rip Currents, and Lateral Currents

Undertows are backwash currents that occur when the water of an incoming wave flows out from a beach. Undertows in wave pools are similar to those at ocean beaches. The greater the slope of the beach or the size of the wave, the greater the strength of the undertow.

The combined force of the incoming wave and the outgoing backwash current can knock you down, especially when loose sand is the only footing available. You are then carried outward, usually to deeper water. Here are the steps in self-rescue from an undertow:
✓ Stay calm — it will make self-rescue easier when the next incoming wave carries you back to shore.
✓ Regain your footing when you are carried back to shore.

Rip currents occur when water accumulates near shore because it can't return outward. The water returns seaward where there is a break in the surfline, for example, between two sandbars or in an underwater gully. A rip current's strength depends on how much water is returning to sea and how big an opening the water tries to pass through. There are several indicators of rip currents:
❑ a break in the surfline
❑ darker water (because of the reduced wave motion on the surface of the current)
❑ an area that looks muddy (because the water is carrying so much sand).

Rip currents are the most dangerous hazard at ocean beaches. The steps in self-rescue from them are as follows:
❑ Don't fight the current — rip currents weaken and dissipate as they head seaward.
❑ Swim across the current and back to safety.

Lateral (side) currents often feed into rip currents. Lateral currents can be dangerous because they can carry unsuspecting bathers out of their depth, into a hazardous area or even into a rip current. Too often, people don't recognize that they're travelling in a lateral current. *All* swimmers, body surfers, and waders should periodically confirm their location relative to onshore landmarks. Because lateral currents usually flow parallel to shore, self-rescue consists of swimming either toward or away from shore.

Self-rescue from River and Hydraulic Currents

Never underestimate the power of a *river current* — even one that seems slow. You can find yourself swept into a river current when a boat overturns or a river bank suddenly collapses. Here are some tips on how to rescue yourself from river currents:

❑ Don't fight the current.
❑ Turn onto your back, and try to stay at the surface.
❑ Move, feet first, with the current.
❑ Scan for and avoid obstacles and debris ahead.
❑ Manoeuvre diagonally out of the current to shore.

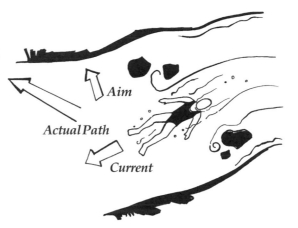

Escaping from a river current

Hydraulic currents are recirculating currents that occur near low-head dams. The tops of these dams are below the water surface. These dams *look* innocent, but they are very dangerous, particularly because the recirculating current at the base of the downstream side of the dam is hard to see from upstream. This current holds anything or anyone, and it is almost impossible to get out of the current without help.

Here are the steps in self-rescue from such currents:

✓ Stay calm, and don't fight the current.
✓ Grab onto and hold a large object such as a rock or a boat, and wait for help.
✓ Look for and avoid becoming entangled in debris, which is often trapped in hydraulic currents. Tree branches are often found in such currents, and they are particularly dangerous.
✓ If you can't grab onto a boat or other large object,
  ● swim underwater, at the bottom of the hydraulic current, and away from the dam. Allow the current to carry you to the dam and to pull you under. When you get to the bottom, swim *with* the downstream current to safety. You might have to try this several times before you succeed.

OR

  ● try to move to shore along the face of the dam. This *might* work, but only if the shore is close enough and someone is there to help you over the dam's vertical wall or onto shore.

3.4   Follow-up and Evaluation

Once you're out of immediate danger, you need to decide what further action is needed. Here are some questions to help you with this:

❑ Do you need medical or other help? Should the incident be reported? (See page 3-3.)

❑ Can bystanders be of any help? (See page 4-2.)

❑ Do you need first aid? (See Chapters 6, 7, and 8.)

It is also important to evaluate self-rescues and learn from them. Go over the rescue from beginning to end. Review every element in the rescue process (see page 3-2), and ask yourself questions like these:

❑ *Recognize.* How accurately and how fast did you recognize that you were in trouble?

❑ *Assess.* How effective was your assessment? Did you choose the safest rescue possible? Did you change your assessment as conditions changed?

❑ *Act.* How well did you perform the self-rescue? How can you improve your self-rescue efforts? How and why did this incident happen? What could prevent such incidents in the future?

3.5   Want to Know More?

American Red Cross. *Canoeing and Kayaking*. United States: The American National Red Cross, 1982.
> This text provides an introduction to safe canoeing and kayaking. Included in the text is information on paddling environments (rivers, currents, etc.), techniques, and self-rescue skills using canoes and kayaks.

Bechdel, Les, and Slim Ray. *River Rescue*, second edition. Boston: Appalachian Mountain Club Books, 1989.
> This is an indispensible aid for anyone who spends time on rivers. It contains clear instructions and high-quality drawings and photographs covering accident prevention and steps to take if accidents do happen. Self-rescue, rescue equipment, patient care and evacuation, and many other topics are covered.

Canadian Canoe Association. *Sprint Racing Canoeing: Level 1 Coaching Certification*. Ottawa: Canadian Canoe Association, 1984.
> This manual is designed for people who are just starting to coach canoeing or kayaking. The purpose of the manual is to provide new coaches with the information they need to ensure safe, fun practices for their athletes. Topics covered include safety, equipment, the planning of practices, basic skills, and basic rules. Each chapter finishes with a self-test, and the answers to all the self-tests are in the manual.

Canadian Canoe Association. *Sprint Racing Canoeing: Level 2 Coaching Certification*. Ottawa: Canadian Canoe Association, 1985.
> This manual extends the information presented in *Sprint Racing Canoeing: Level 1 Coaching Certification* (see immediately above). Both manuals are designed mainly for coaches, with the Level 2 manual focusing on how to help athletes achieve higher performance levels. Information on advanced training and technique is presented, as is basic information on strength training and the prevention and care of injuries. Goal setting is also emphasized in the manual.

Chapter 4
The Rescue of Others

4.1 Introduction

Rescues involving others can be physically and emotionally demanding for both rescuer and victim. This chapter covers the skills needed to perform safe, effective, and efficient rescues. The recurring theme is the rescue process, which involves the following three elements:

✓ Recognize
✓ Assess
✓ Act.

The rescue process is used in self-rescue, the rescue of others, and first aid. The three elements are the same in every kind of rescue or first aid situation, but the element details are different. See Chapter 3 for how the process applies to self-rescue, Chapter 6 for how it applies to first aid.

Your safety is your primary and ongoing priority in a rescue. Two "tools" presented in this chapter will help you in your assessments and actions. The Ladder Approach to rescues helps you assess the situation and choose the safest rescue possible. The Rescuer's Checklist is a guide to the actions appropriate for the rescue you've chosen.

This chapter provides you with the *knowledge* so vital to developing good *judgment* in rescues. Practising the techniques covered here will help you develop and refine the *skill* you need to rescue others. When you add personal *fitness*, you have it all — the four components of water rescue!

4.2   The Rescue of Others: The Rescue Process

This section summarizes the rescue process as it applies to the rescue of others. The process applies to all such rescues, and it's dynamic. You repeat its elements again and again until you're out of the water, and you go through them again once you're out of the water. In some cases, you may recognize-assess-act many times, changing the procedures you choose as conditions change. It all depends on the rescue situation.

Recognize

✓ Recognize that someone is in trouble, and that you must perform a rescue.
✓ Recognize that aspects of the situation, such as your condition, the victim's condition, or water and weather conditions, may change.
✓ Recognize hazards, the cause of the incident, and the number of victims and their condition.

Using Bystanders
During a rescue, you have many actions to perform. Bystanders can help you by
✓ calling for medical help or other assistance
✓ helping you remove the victim from the water
✓ getting blankets, first aid supplies, or other equipment
✓ helping with first aid
✓ helping to manage crowds that form
✓ waiting for emergency services and directing them to the accident scene
✓ writing down details of first aid treatment.

Instructing Bystanders
In dealing with bystanders,
✓ ask for help
✓ identify the bystander(s) to whom you're speaking
✓ find out if bystanders have any lifesaving or first aid training — trained bystanders can usually do more sophisticated tasks than untrained ones
✓ give clear, specific directions
✓ speak slowly and firmly, and control your voice
✓ ask them to report to you when they've finished their task
✓ thank them when it's all over.

Assess
Here are some of the questions to ask yourself when assessing a situation:
✓ What self-rescue skills does the victim have?
✓ What rescue skills and physical skills do you have?
✓ What is the victim's physical and emotional condition?
✓ Where is the closest point of safety?
✓ What are the water and weather conditions? How will they affect your options?
✓ What human and equipment assistance is available?
✓ What is the lowest risk rescue possible in the situation?

Act
Act is the third element of the rescue process (see page 4-1). Given your assessment, choose your option before you start (see Section 4.4) and carry it out as well as you can. If you recognize that conditions are changing, reassess your options and change your actions as needed:
✓ Do the things you decided to do in your assessment.
✓ Direct bystanders as needed.
✓ Contact the Emergency Medical System (EMS) if you need it (see page 3-3).
✓ Contact the authorities if the incident should be reported.

The next sections discuss the following elements of the rescue process in detail:
- ❏ victim recognition
- ❏ the Ladder Approach
- ❏ the Rescuer's Checklist
- ❏ hazards
- ❏ assists
- ❏ entries
- ❏ approaches
- ❏ reverse, ready, and reassess
- ❏ talk, tow, or carry
- ❏ removals
- ❏ follow-up.

Expectations for Lifesavers and Lifeguards

Lifesavers and lifeguards are both important rescuers, but the expectations for each group are different.

Lifesavers are trained in what to do, but the situations they find themselves in can vary greatly. The environment, equipment, and available personnel are not plannable in a lifesaving situation.

Lifeguards, however, are undertaking a responsibility to have the knowledge, skill, fitness, and judgment needed to prevent accidents and perform rescues. They know their specific facility and have practised how to work together with available staff and equipment in various circumstances.

4.3   Victim Recognition

As a lifesaver, you must *recognize* when someone is in danger of drowning. Here are just some of the signs this is happening:
- ✓ fear on the face of someone close to shore
- ✓ lack of progress of a swimmer
- ✓ a distressed call for help
- ✓ an overturned boat
- ✓ an inflatable toy moving away
- ✓ a crowd gathering.

People in danger of drowning may be either
- ❏ distressed swimmers or
- ❏ drowning victims.

Distressed swimmers can be novice swimmers with limited swimming ability, tired or weak swimmers, and people who are ill or injured. This group also includes swimmers who become disoriented after playing in or falling into the water. Unless they are rescued, distressed swimmers can become drowning victims.

Tired or weak swimmer

Distressed swimmer

**Drowning victim
(unconscious)**

Does the Victim Want Your Help?

The issue of a victim giving consent to be helped is a complex one. In a rescue situation, you will have to use judgment in this area. Discuss (with your instructor, your family doctor, and others) the situations, if any, in which it might be reasonable to act in a manner different from the expressed or perceived wishes of the victim. In all rescue situations, you should identify yourself and say what you're going to do. For instance, say "Stay calm. My name is _____, and I'm going to help you get to shore."

While there are variations from person to person, the keys to recognizing distressed swimmers are the following:
- ❏ Their body position approaches the vertical.
- ❏ They are making little forward progress.
- ❏ Distress is obvious on their face.
- ❏ They are breathing, and so they may call or wave for help.
- ❏ If they are injured or ill, they might be holding the affected area of the body.
- ❏ They may be facing a point they consider "safety," such as the shore, a raft, a boat, or a dock.

Drowning victims are unable to support themselves at the surface. They are *not* always non-swimmers, and they may or may not struggle against drowning. Many factors can prevent people from struggling — illness, injury (a blow to the head, for instance), alcohol or other intoxicants, hyperventilation (people who hyperventilate become unconscious without a struggle), fatigue, or unconsciousness.

Those who *do* struggle against drowning stay on or near the surface for only a short time. In addition, they
- ❏ are probably vertical in the water; they do not use their legs for propulsion.
- ❏ show fear on their face.
- ❏ may seem to be playing in the water. This is because of their arm movements.
- ❏ *cannot* call for help. They need all the air they breathe to stay alive.
- ❏ *cannot* control their reaction to struggle.
- ❏ may not be moving at all.
- ❏ may not be visible (because they are submerged).

**Drowning victim
(non-swimmer)**

4.4   The Ladder Approach

There are many decisions to make when someone is in danger of drowning. In assessing what to do, you must know your options and choose appropriate actions from them. These options are summarized in the *Ladder Approach* to rescues. Before you do anything as a rescuer, choose the safest rescue possible — consider the ladder.

In rescues, you do NOT have to do everything yourself. Bystanders can be a great help (see page 4-2), and the possibility of such help is an important factor in your assessment.

 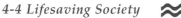

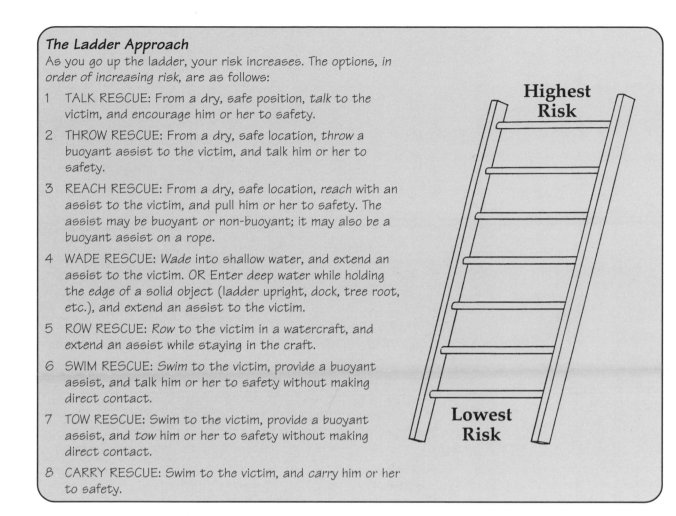

The Ladder Approach

As you go up the ladder, your risk increases. The options, *in order of increasing risk*, are as follows:

1 TALK RESCUE: From a dry, safe position, *talk* to the victim, and encourage him or her to safety.

2 THROW RESCUE: From a dry, safe location, *throw* a buoyant assist to the victim, and talk him or her to safety.

3 REACH RESCUE: From a dry, safe location, *reach* with an assist to the victim, and pull him or her to safety. The assist may be buoyant or non-buoyant; it may also be a buoyant assist on a rope.

4 WADE RESCUE: *Wade* into shallow water, and extend an assist to the victim. OR Enter deep water while holding the edge of a solid object (ladder upright, dock, tree root, etc.), and extend an assist to the victim.

5 ROW RESCUE: *Row* to the victim in a watercraft, and extend an assist while staying in the craft.

6 SWIM RESCUE: *Swim* to the victim, provide a buoyant assist, and talk him or her to safety without making direct contact.

7 TOW RESCUE: Swim to the victim, provide a buoyant assist, and *tow* him or her to safety without making direct contact.

8 CARRY RESCUE: Swim to the victim, and *carry* him or her to safety.

Highest Risk

Lowest Risk

The Ladder Approach to water rescue presents, *in order of increasing risk*, your options for helping someone in trouble in the water (see illustration above).

As a rescuer, you should always choose the rescue method that involves the least amount of risk. The first "rung" on the ladder is a Talk Rescue — you encourage the victim to safety *without even entering the water*.

As a rescuer, you move up the rungs of the ladder *only if*
❏ you have the knowledge, judgment, skill, and fitness to accept the greater risk involved
❏ the victim's condition worsens
❏ suitable assists are available for use
❏ the environmental conditions change.

The Rungs of the Ladder

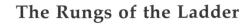

Talk Rescue

✓ From a dry, safe location, provide positive verbal support with clear, simple instructions about what to do.
✓ From a crouched position, tell the victim to "watch me, keep your head up, kick your feet, and grab the side."
✓ Eye contact and positive encouragement can have immediate results on a victim at close range, without putting you in any danger.

Throw Rescue

✓ If the victim is a short distance from shore and a suitable buoyant object is available, throw the object so the victim can grasp it for support.
✓ Be careful not to hit the victim on the head when throwing the object.
✓ Encourage the victim verbally, and direct him or her toward safety.
✓ Remember that wind and waves make it harder to throw with accuracy.

Reach Rescue

✓ If you can find a suitable rescue assist, extend it, and pull the victim to safety.

✓ If the victim is close enough, a towel might do the trick. For victims farther away, a pole or a branch works well. You can reach even farther if a rope is attached to the buoyant object.
✓ Buoyant objects are usually best, because they support victims in the water. This means you don't have to lift *and* pull.
✓ Keep your centre of gravity as low as possible. Anchor yourself by holding onto a solid object such as a tree root, ladder, or dock with your free hand. This will help prevent you from being pulled into the water.

Wade Rescue

#4 Wade

✓ When the victim cannot be reached from shore, wade into the water with a rescue assist, and extend it to the victim.

✓ Keep risk as low as possible by keeping your feet on the solid bottom at all times or by grasping a solid object (ladder upright, dock, tree root, etc.) with your free hand.

✓ If there are several rescuers, you can form a human chain by taking hold of one another's wrists. The rescuer nearest the victim extends the assist and encourages the victim. Another rescuer acts as leader and guides the "chain" back to shore.

Row Rescue

#5 Row

This rescue involves greater risk because you do it in open water from a small boat (rowboat, canoe, etc.). Page 4-8 summarizes the pros and cons of using different small boats in rescues.

> It's a good idea to learn how to operate small boats. If you use them in a rescue, you'll need to know the provincial or territorial regulations and comply with them.

✓ Try to manoeuvre the boat so that you approach the victim with wind in your face. This reduces the chances of the boat being pushed into the victim and injuring him or her. But if you're alone in a strong wind, you may need to approach from the windward side.

Approach with wind in your face

✓ Apply the principles of the Ladder Approach from the boat as you would on land. First talk to the victim, and then throw him or her a lifejacket, PFD, or boat cushion. If the victim needs further support, pull on the object to bring the victim in, or offer a paddle or throwing line.

✓ Once the victim has the assist securely in his or her grasp, decide whether to row to shore with the victim in the water or to put the victim in the boat. The decision you make will depend on the victim's condition and size, the boat's stability, your distance from shore, the water temperature, your boating skill, and the number of rescuers.

Small Boats in Rescues

Here are the key pros and cons of using different small boats in rescues:

- ❏ **Canoes.** Canoes can be quite unstable. This is why only experienced canoeists should use canoes for a rescue. It is hard to get a victim into a canoe when the water is calm and almost impossible to do so in rough water.
- ❏ **Inflatable Boats.** The stability of these boats varies. Those powered by outboard motors can be easily manoeuvred in many water and weather conditions. They make rescue easy and comfortable for both rescuers and victims.
- ❏ **Kayaks, Rowing Sculls, Paddleboards, Etc.** Kayaks and rowing sculls usually have limited stability. But victims can often hold onto them while being towed to safety, and rescuers can also use them as a "buoyant assist" while supporting a victim in the water. Paddleboards are convenient for short-distance rescues and buoyant enough to support two people. Paddleboards can also be used as a buoyant assist, and you can, if necessary, start rescue breathing while holding the board.
- ❏ **Powerboats.** Small outboard motors (5-25 horsepower) provide adequate power and are adaptable enough to make a small powerboat a useful rescue device. When near the victim, cut the power to avoid injuring him or her.
- ❏ **Rowboats.** Rowboats are easy to manoeuvre, and they are very stable. Boats with a square stern are best for rescues, because it's easy to help a conscious person climb aboard. If necessary, rescue breathing can be applied from the stern and the victim lifted into the boat as resuscitation continues.
- ❏ **Sailboards.** Only skilled boardsailors should use these craft in rescues. Without their sails, sailboards can be used like paddleboards (see above).
- ❏ **Sailboats.** It takes experience and skill to operate a sailboat well enough to use it in rescues — to stop where the victim is, manoeuvre the boat into position, and head directly into the wind. The stability of sailboats varies. Generally, the stern is the best place to deal with a victim.
- ❏ **Water Scooters.** These small motorized craft are fast and manoeuvrable. Typically intended for one rider, scooters could be used to transport a second person to safety in an emergency. They could also be used as large "buoyant assists" until further help arrives.

Swim Rescue

#6 Swim The following circumstances may make it necessary for you to enter the water during a rescue:

- ❏ The victim's condition gets worse.
- ❏ The victim is too far away to reach with a throwing assist.
- ❏ You've tried to throw an assist but haven't succeeded.
- ❏ No small craft is available.

In a swim rescue,

- ✓ enter the water with a buoyant assist, and swim to the victim.
- ✓ minimize your personal risk by pushing the assist to the victim *from the ready position* (see page 4-19). Avoid even *indirect* contact with the victim.
- ✓ back up in a ready position, maintain eye contact, and encourage the victim to safety.

The success of this kind of rescue depends on the victim's ability to hold the assist and support his or her head above the water's surface. It is important to learn about and be skilled in defences and releases before practising swim rescues.

Tow Rescue

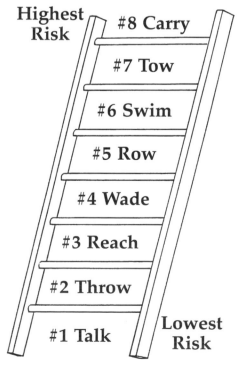

If you've tried a swim rescue and the victim cannot move to safety while holding an assist, pull from the other end of the assist and tow the victim to safety.

This indirect contact with the victim brings you very close to him or her, and it increases your personal risk. To ensure your own safety, be ready to move away quickly at any time.

Carry Rescue

Direct contact between rescuer and victim may be required when
  ✓ the victim cannot support his or her head above the surface while holding an assist
✓ no assist is available, and the victim is not responding to verbal encouragement
✓ the victim is unconscious.

Drowning victims need support to clear their mouth above the water's surface and get air. Victims may see an approaching rescuer as a high, stable object and seize him or her to get the needed support. Contact rescues without a buoyant assist present the greatest risk to rescuers.

Here are some key principles of contact rescues:
❑ No matter how skilled a rescuer you are, direct contact with victims should be chosen *last*, after you've tried or ruled out all the other "rungs" on the ladder.
❑ Try this kind of rescue *only if you are trained and fit to do so.*
❑ Talk to the victim throughout the rescue to calm and reassure him or her as much as possible. Tell the victim what you are doing and what you are going to do.
❑ Maintain eye contact when approaching the victim, and watch him or her closely at all times.
❑ Whenever possible, contact the victim from behind — it's safer. Act quickly and effectively to take full control of the victim. Some rescuers expect victims to turn around on command — this is unrealistic.
❑ Take control of the victim from the moment of contact. Do this to provide support and air for the victim, not to subdue him or her. Be ready to move away if necessary.
❑ If possible, have someone else ready to provide immediate support if help is needed.
❑ If you have to change your carrying technique, maintain victim control.

Highest Risk

#8 Carry

#7 Tow

#6 Swim

#5 Row

#4 Wade

#3 Reach

#2 Throw

#1 Talk

Lowest Risk

4.5 The Rescuer's Checklist

How do you actually *carry out* your rescue? In any rescue other than a talk rescue, there are lots of ways to *reach* a victim, different methods to *swim* to a victim, and many ways to *carry* a victim. This raises two questions: How do you decide? And how do you do it once you've decided?

Use the *Rescuer's Checklist* to answer the first question. The Rescuer's Checklist is a guide to action. *Wherever you are on the ladder*, use the checklist to review your options on that rung and choose the appropriate option.

Here are the items in the Rescuer's Checklist, as well as guidelines to help you choose the appropriate option:

> In any rescue, treat the victim *as an individual*. Take into account factors such as his or her abilities (including physical or learning disabilities). Modify techniques as necessary.

✓ HAZARDS. *Before doing anything else*, deal with items in the environment that could be dangerous for you or the victim. Either remove these hazards from the environment or move the victim away from the hazards.

✓ ASSISTS. Always enter water with an assist — it limits your risk. Buoyant objects are best, but any suitable substitute will do (see page 4-12). Choose portable assists of appropriate size. If you cannot use the assist, leave it aside.

✓ ENTRIES. The entry you choose depends on water depth and on the victim's location and condition. It also depends on your personal knowledge of the water bottom and on the assists available for use.

✓ APPROACHES. If the victim can hear, shout encouragement to him or her. If you have to swim, use a head-up stroke to maintain both visual and verbal contact with the victim.

✓ REVERSE, READY, AND REASSESS. When you are 2 or 3 metres from the victim, reverse, and take a "ready" position. Push the assist to the victim, and talk to him or her while reassessing the situation.

✓ TALK, TOW, OR CARRY. From your ready position, decide whether the victim can reach safety on his or her own by using the assist while you encourage him or her. If this isn't possible, intervene, and use either a tow or a carry. Choose the safest method that suits the victim and the water conditions. Make contact only if the victim cannot hold the assist or is unconscious.

✓ REMOVALS. Remove victims from the water as soon as possible, and use the removal method with the least risk *for you and the victim*.

✓ FOLLOW-UP. Once the victim is out of immediate physical danger, evaluate his or her condition, and start follow-up procedures. If possible, get help moving the victim to a comfortable environment. Call EMS if necessary. Decide whether the incident should be formally reported to an authority.

How the Ladder Approach and Rescuer's Checklist Work Together

The chart below shows the relationship between the Rescuer's Checklist and the Ladder Approach. It shows, for example, that removing hazards is part of every rescue. Similarly, follow-up must happen in every rescue. But reverse, ready, and reassess occurs only in swim, tow, and carry rescues.

Rescuer's Checklist	*The Ladder Approach*							
	Talk	*Throw*	*Reach*	*Wade*	*Row*	*Swim*	*Tow*	*Carry*
Hazards	✓	✓	✓	✓	✓	✓	✓	✓
Assists		✓	✓	✓	✓	✓	✓	✓
Entries				✓		✓	✓	✓
Approaches					✓	✓	✓	✓
Reverse, Ready, and Reassess						✓	✓	✓
Talk, Tow, or Carry						✓	✓	✓
Removals	✓	✓	✓	✓	✓	✓	✓	✓
Follow-up	✓	✓	✓	✓	✓	✓	✓	✓

The next sections describe each element of the Rescuer's Checklist in detail.

4.6 Hazards ✔

In any rescue situation, there may be *hazards* in the environment that could endanger you or cause further danger to the victim. Either remove such hazards from the area or remove the victim from the hazards.

Common hazards include
❏ water
❏ poisonous gas, such as engine exhaust or chlorine gas
❏ other types of poisons
❏ live electrical wires
❏ debris, such as broken glass
❏ extreme cold or heat
❏ animals.

> ### Reducing Stress in Rescues
> Rescues can be stressful for you *and* the victim. Here are some things you can do to reduce your stress during and after rescues:
> ✓ Practise simulated rescue situations.
> ✓ Mentally rehearse rescue situations.
> ✓ Keep physically fit.
> ✓ Practise your rescue skills.
> ✓ Update your knowledge and skills *regularly*.
>
> See Appendix A for more information on how to deal with stress reactions to rescues.
>
> And here are some things you can do to reduce *victims'* stress:
> ✓ Identify yourself, and learn victims' names.
> ✓ Talk to victims calmly and reassuringly.
> ✓ Hold victims securely during water rescues.
> ✓ Make decisive body movements.
> ✓ Keep victims' faces above water.

4.7   Assists ✔

An *assist* is any object that can be used to help someone in difficulty in the water.

Possible Assists

Possible assists include the following:

- ❏ *lifejackets and PFDs.* Because of their buoyancy, lifejackets and PFDs are excellent assists.
- ❏ *kickboards.* Kickboards (flutterboards) are used as assists in many facilities because they are so widely available. They are, however, hard to throw and tend to blow away.
- ❏ *improvised buoyant assists.* Buoyant objects such as plastic bottles (for example, bleach containers), plastic coolers, gasoline containers, oars, paddles, boards, and branches can all be used in rescues. Poles, oars, paddles, and sticks make excellent extensions because they are usually light and strong and can be extended with accuracy.
- ❏ *reaching poles.* Reaching poles are used when the victim is within reaching distance. These poles vary in length and are made of various materials. Some models are very light, and some are electrically insulated. Reaching poles that are hooked are called "shepherd's hooks."
- ❏ *ring buoys.* Ring buoys are required at public pools and beaches by regulation in many regions in Canada. They are also found at many docks and marinas. A length of rope allows them to be thrown to someone at a distance.
- ❏ *rescue cans.* Rescue cans (torpedo buoys) come with a length of rope and a strap that slips over the rescuer's shoulder. Cans are rigid and easy to hold onto; they can be used as reaching assists or as assists to tow or carry distressed swimmers or drowning victims.
- ❏ *rescue tubes.* Rescue tubes are similar in shape to rescue cans, but they are made of soft foam with a waterproof coating. They have an attached shoulder loop and line at one end, a snap at the other. The tube can be wrapped around a victim and secured with the snap. Because they have no handles, rescue tubes can be hard for victims to hold onto.
- ❏ *throw bags.* Throw bags are generally a white-water assist. They consist of a bag with a length of rope. The rope comes out of the bag while it is in "flight." With practice, you can throw these bags both far and accurately.

Choosing an Assist

When choosing an assist, consider

- ✓ *availability.* The assist must be *readily* available.
- ✓ *buoyancy.* Floating objects support victims higher in the water and allow *you* to rest as needed.

 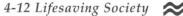

✓ *manageability*. The assist must be easy to handle on land and in the water, and it should add little or no resistance on your approach.

✓ *strength*. The assist must be strong enough for the task at hand.

✓ *your fitness and strength*. Be sure you can carry and use the assist effectively. If you don't, you could be putting yourself in danger.

✓ *your immediate surroundings*. The assist you choose should "fit" the surroundings. While a reaching pole is long, for example, it's harder to man-oeuvre if there are people nearby. It's also harder to manoeuvre if there's a fence or wall close to the water's edge — you can't pull a long pole in all the way. A smaller or shorter object is more suitable when the victim is close to shore.

Using an Assist

You can use assists either by extending them or by throwing them.

When *extending* an assist, keep your centre of gravity as low as possible to avoid being pulled into the water by the victim. Take care not to jab the struggling victim with the assist. After extending the assist, crouch or drop to one knee, staying as far from the water's edge as the length of the assist permits. Drawing the assist in hand-over-hand, move gradually to the edge to secure the victim.

Shirts and Pants as Towing Assists

❏ While PFDs or lifejackets are much more effective, some clothing items make useful towing assists.

❏ During your approach, swim with pants or a shirt on your shoulders, with the legs or sleeves stretched forward over your shoulders and back under your arms.

❏ Use clothes to tow a calm, passive victim. From behind the victim, pass the legs or sleeves under his or her arms and back over his or her shoulders. (You are using clothes much as you use your arms in a modified body carry (see page 4-23).) Hold both legs or sleeves in one hand during the tow, and use your other arm to scull or fin.

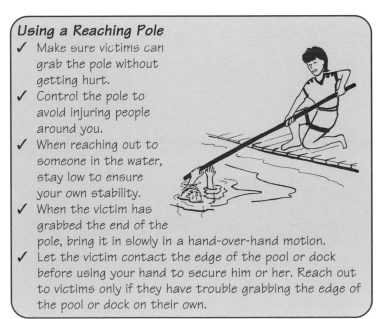

Using a Reaching Pole

✓ Make sure victims can grab the pole without getting hurt.

✓ Control the pole to avoid injuring people around you.

✓ When reaching out to someone in the water, stay low to ensure your own stability.

✓ When the victim has grabbed the end of the pole, bring it in slowly in a hand-over-hand motion.

✓ Let the victim contact the edge of the pool or dock before using your hand to secure him or her. Reach out to victims only if they have trouble grabbing the edge of the pool or dock on their own.

If the victim is *just* out of reach, you can lie down to stretch out as far as possible:

✓ Lie down at an angle of about 45° to the side of the dock or pool with your legs spread. This position is most stable, because your centre of gravity is as low as possible. The angled position places one shoulder over the edge of the dock or pool, allowing freedom of movement and offering the longest reach.

If reaching poles or buoyant assists are not readily available, you can use non-floating materials such as clothing, towels, or blankets to reach out to victims:

✓ Lie down as described above.
✓ Extend the assist to the victim.

This type of assist is harder to extend because it is flexible and must be "flipped" to the victim. This makes placement less precise and may slow down the rescue.

If *no* assist is available, you can reach directly with an arm or a leg from the prone position described above. Keep a firm hold on the pool edge, dock, or boat. Because there is greater risk when making direct contact with a victim, use an arm or leg extension *only when reaching assists are not readily available.*

Pendulum swing

When *throwing* an assist (rope, ring buoy, throw bag, etc.),

✓ secure the trailing end of the rope. For example, make a knot at one end, and place it under one foot or tie it to the dock.
✓ consider currents and other factors that could affect your throw. If you are throwing an assist in a current, throw upstream so that the assist follows the current to the victim.
✓ throw past the victim, and use a pendulum swing. For maximum distance, release assists at a 45° angle (compared with the horizontal).
✓ drop to one knee or lie flat on your stomach after throwing. This increases your stability.
✓ pull the assist back slowly and hand-over-hand once the victim has it.
✓ let the victim contact the edge of the pool or dock before using your hand to secure him or her. Reach out to victims only if they have trouble grabbing the edge of the pool or dock on their own.

Here are some tips on specific assists:

❏ To improve your throwing accuracy with rope, attach a lightly weighted, buoyant object to the throwing end of the line. An example of such an object is a semi-filled plastic container (a bleach container, for instance).

❏ Throwing ropes should always be ready for use in emergencies. It's a good idea to have such ropes permanently knotted and uniformly coiled — that way, you lose less time in emergencies.

4.8   Entries ✔

Emergency situations can require a rapid entry into the water for searches and rescues in varying circumstances. You need to know different ways of entering the water — that way, you can choose the best one for the situation.

Possible Entries

❏ Wading or running
❏ Slip-in entry
❏ Stride jump
❏ Head-up dive
❏ Shallow dive
❏ Compact jump
❏ Modified compact jump

Wading or Running

If the water is shallow but you aren't sure of the water conditions in the area,

✓ consider keeping your shoes on
✓ wade in slowly and carefully
✓ go to the victim by sliding your feet along the bottom, testing the depth with a reaching assist, stick, or pole
✓ test the bottom for firmness and underwater obstructions before transferring your weight to the front foot.

If the water is shallow and you *know* the area's water conditions,

✓ run to the victim if conditions permit, swinging your legs sideways to clear the surface as water depth increases.

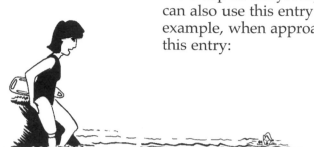

Slip-in Entry

If the water is deep and you're unsure of the water conditions, use a slip-in entry. Any other entry is extremely dangerous. You can also use this entry if you want to minimize movement (for example, when approaching injured victims). Here's how to do this entry:

✓ Place one or both hands at the point of entry, and use your arms to lower yourself slowly and deliberately, feet first, into the water.
✓ Maintain visual and verbal contact with the victim.

Stride Jump

The goal of this entry is to jump as far as possible while looking at the victim. Your head does *not* go under the water. This is NOT an entry for unknown or shallow water or for heights greater than 1 metre.

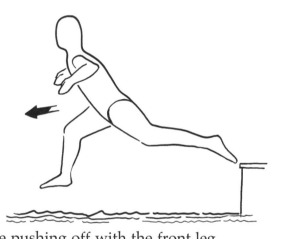

✓ Start from a standing position at the edge of a pool, dock, deck, etc.
✓ The legs are astride, and the knees are slightly bent.
✓ Angle the trunk forward from the waist, and hold the head erect.
✓ Take a long stride, stepping through with the back leg while pushing off with the front leg.
✓ The trunk stays angled forward as both arms swing over the shoulders to the front of the body to press down against the water on entry. The action of the legs and the momentum of the arms enable you to cover the greatest distance before entry.
✓ On entry, use a strong scissor kick to stop the momentum of the jump and to start to lift the lower body into a horizontal position for the approach to the victim.
✓ Angle the upper body forward to increase forward momentum and ease the change into the swimming position.

Head-up Dive

This dive is faster than the stride jump, because you enter the water in a position that lets you start swimming earlier. This dive also allows you to keep victims in your sight. Because of the head-up position on entry, this dive is used only from a very limited height (15 centimetres or less). This is NOT an entry for unknown or shallow water.

✓ Start from a standing position at the edge of a pool, dock, deck, etc.
✓ The legs are together, and the knees are slightly bent.
✓ Angle the upper body forward from the waist, and hold the head erect.
✓ Swing the arms forward, and push off with both legs, arching the back and stretching the hands out in front.

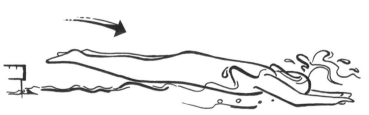

✓ In flight, the body is in a diagonal position.
✓ First contact with the water is made by the lower legs. Resistance starts to reduce your speed, and you enter the water with a rocking motion caused by the action-reaction of the entry. The hands slap the water, pressing down to prevent submersion.
✓ Don't stop after your entry — take your first swimming stroke as soon as you can.

Shallow Dive

The depth of water required for a *safe* shallow dive depends on your skill in shallow dives. A *minimum* of 1 metre (3 feet) is recommended for skilled divers. Under stress, however, your judgment about whether the depth is safe may be affected. There are documented cases of spinal injuries in which skilled divers dove into water between 3 and 4 feet deep.

When you know the water is free of underwater hazards and is deep enough, a shallow dive is an appropriate entry. It is faster than the stride jump, because you are in a streamlined position. Its disadvantage is that you lose sight of the victim.

✓ Start from a standing position at the edge of a pool, dock, deck, etc.
✓ The feet are slightly apart.
✓ The knees and hips are bent so that you are crouched and your back is roughly parallel to the water.
✓ Throw your arms forward forcefully while pushing off with the legs.

✓ In flight, the head drops slightly between the outstretched arms and the body is fully extended.
✓ Try to make your dive as shallow as possible. Stay streamlined as long as you can, and then start to swim.

Compact Jump
This jump is used to enter the water from a great height, such as from a wharf. This is NOT an entry for unknown or shallow water.

✓ Cross the legs, and keep the arms close to the body.
✓ Cross the arms across the chest, placing one hand over the mouth and nose.
✓ Once underwater, use the arms and legs to stop downward motion.
✓ Surface, and swim to the victim.

Modified Compact Jump
This entry is used from an intermediate height — 1 to 1½ metres. This entry is useful when victims are close to the edge of a pool, dock, or boat or when they are in the deep end of a wave pool. This entry keeps your head above the surface, and you always see the victim. Since the jump's vertical descent eliminates the forward motion of the stride jump, the entry doesn't swamp victims. This is NOT an entry for unknown or shallow water.

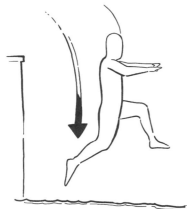

✓ Start from a standing position at the edge of a pool, dock, deck, etc.
✓ The legs are straddled, the knees are slightly bent, and the upper body is straight.
✓ Step off the edge, and drop straight down.
✓ Do a whip kick on contact with the water.
✓ Reduce downward pressure by pressing on the water with the hands and arms.
✓ Move to a horizontal position, and swim to the victim.

Choosing an Entry
Consider the following when choosing your entry:
❏ the victim's condition and location
❏ your abilities
❏ your condition and location
❏ water conditions (depth, currents, waves, temperature, pollution, etc.)
❏ the condition of the bottom
❏ the speed with which you need to get to the victim
❏ the need to keep the victim in sight
❏ the assists available for use
❏ your familiarity with the area.

4.9   Approaches ✔

It's important to reach victims as fast as possible. Use your most efficient stroke, given the water conditions and the assist being used. Possible approaches include head-up front crawl and head-up breaststroke. Head-up approaches let you maintain visual and verbal contact with victims.

Choosing an Approach

Take these factors into account:
❏ the victim's condition
❏ your abilities
❏ environmental conditions
❏ your familiarity with water conditions in the area. Remember that head-up breaststroke keeps you more horizontal in unknown water.

Carrying Assists during Approaches

✓ When swimming, an assist with a line is most easily towed. If this isn't possible, hold the assist in front with one hand, and use your most efficient stroke to swim to the victim.

✓ You can drape clothing or a towel across your neck and over your shoulders. This leaves both arms free for swimming. Do this only if it doesn't interfere with breathing or swimming.

✓ You can grip a buoyant assist such as a flutterboard between your legs on dive entries. Be sure to cross your legs at the ankles.

✓ Before starting your approach, remove any heavy clothing (lightweight clothing probably won't seriously hinder good swimmers). In most cases, shoes should be removed before you enter the water.

✓ When you plan to use clothing as a reaching or towing assist, it might be preferable to 1) *wear* the item during your approach, 2) reverse and ready (see below), and 3) remove it when you're a safe distance from the victim. This is often faster than swimming while carrying clothing in one hand.

4.10   Reverse, Ready, and Reassess ✔

When you are 2 to 3 metres from the victim, stop, reverse your direction, assume a "ready" position, and talk to him or her. This position allows you to swim away quickly if you think you'll be grabbed.

"Sit" in the water with one leg bent in front and the foot at the surface. Face the victim, and maintain your stability with a sculling action (see page 9-13). If necessary, use your bent leg to push the victim away, or swim away until he or she is calm.

Ready position

While in your ready position, assess your original plan again. Circumstances may have changed:
❏ The victim's condition may have changed, or your assessment of the victim may have changed:
   ● The victim may have become tired.
   ● A conscious victim may have become unconscious.
   ● A distressed victim may have become a drowning victim.
❏ The victim may be larger or smaller than you had originally thought.
❏ The victim may have injuries or disabilities you weren't aware of.
❏ The victim may not accept a buoyant assist.
❏ The water may have become rougher or calmer.

Once you reassess things, you'll know whether to continue the rescue by talking the victim to safety from your ready position or by using a tow or carry.

4.11 Talk, Tow, or Carry ✔

If possible, *talk* victims to safety. If that isn't possible, tow or carry them. Choose the *safest method,* considering your safety, the victim's condition, and water conditions. Make contact only if victims cannot hold an assist or are unconscious.

While it's easier to tow victims if they are in a horizontal position, it isn't possible every time. Most conscious victims instinctively want to *sit* — it keeps their heads above water — and so you need to try to tow them in this position. Use any suitable kick to move to safety. While towing, keep your eyes on the victim, and *constantly* offer encouragement and reassurance.

Throughout a tow, be ready to release rescue assists or towing lines and swim away if the victim's behaviour becomes unpredictable. If this happens, assume a ready position, and wait until the victim is calm or manageable before continuing the tow.

When the victim's condition makes towing impossible, use a carry. In a carry, *you* hold the victim — he or she doesn't hold you.

Possible Carries

❑ *Assistive carries.* These carries provide you with the most safety but the least control over victims. They allow victims to help while being pulled to safety. Assistive carries are used mainly with victims who are
  ● weak
  ● tired
  ● injured below the waist.
❑ *Control carries.* These carries put you at greatest risk but give you maximum control over victims. In all such carries, keep the victim's head *out of the water.* Control carries are used mainly with victims who are
  ● non-swimmers
  ● in rough water conditions
  ● distressed
  ● injured above or below the waist
  ● unconscious.

Assistive Carries

Any carry that allows the victim to help and provides the most safety for the rescuer can be considered an assistive carry. Some examples are provided below.

❏ Elbow or wrist carry
❏ Clothes carry
❏ Underarm carry
❏ Single-chin carry

Elbow or Wrist Carry. For this carry,

✓ position yourself as for the underarm carry
✓ hold the victim's wrist or elbow, and pull the victim to safety.

Clothes Carry. Technique is as follows:

✓ If the victim is wearing clothes, hold onto them, support the victim's head with the arm holding the clothing, and pull the victim to safety.
✓ Avoid grabbing clothing that could put pressure on the throat and choke the victim.

Underarm Carry. Technique is as follows:

✓ Approach the victim from behind, and place your hand under the victim's shoulder.
✓ With a secure grip, pull the victim to safety while swimming on your side or back.
✓ Use any kick that works.

Single-Chin Carry. For this carry,
✓ get behind the victim, and hold his or her chin with one hand
✓ with a secure grip, provide support, and pull the victim to safety
✓ go only short distances, because victims must hold their neck stiff
✓ DON'T put pressure on the victim's throat.

Control Carries

Any carry that allows you to hold the victim's head out of the water can be considered a control carry. Some examples are provided below.
❏ Head carry
❏ Double-chin carry
❏ Modified body carry
❏ Cross-chest carry

Head Carry. In this carry,
✓ get behind the victim.
✓ place your hands firmly on the side of the victim's head (one hand on each side).
✓ spread your fingers to avoid covering the victim's ears. This avoids further upsetting the victim and lets him or her hear what you're saying.
✓ alternatively, cup the victim's chin with one hand, and put your other hand on the back of his or her head.
✓ pull the victim to safety.

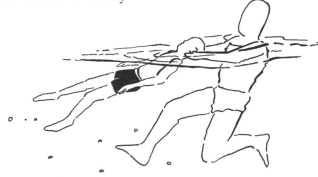

Double-Chin Carry. Technique is as follows:
✓ From behind the victim, cup his or her chin with both your hands.
✓ Place your forearms on the victim's shoulders — it gives you the leverage you need to tilt the victim's head.
✓ Pull the victim to safety, avoiding his or her throat throughout the carry.
✓ To prevent the victim's head from falling back, lift the victim's chin, secure his or her head by gently squeezing with your forearms. Alternatively, put his or her head on your chest.

Modified Body Carry. In this carry,
✓ from behind the victim, pass your arms under the victim's arms
✓ curl your arms, and grab the victim's shoulders or head
✓ using one arm and kicking, pull the victim to safety.

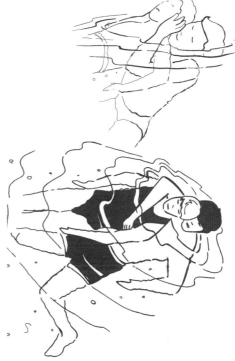

Cross-Chest Carry. Technique is as follows:
✓ From behind, draw the victim close to you by reaching over his or her shoulder, across the chest, and under the far arm.
✓ To increase control, put your wrist under the victim's far armpit — it brings the palm of your hand against the victim's back or shoulder.
✓ Pull the victim to safety, and avoid putting pressure on his or her throat throughout the carry.

Choosing a Carry
✓ When choosing a carry, consider both your swimming skills and the circumstances of the rescue.
✓ Choose a carry that is *efficient*, one that
  ● always keeps the victim's mouth above the surface
  ● gives *you* freedom of movement
  ● provides maximum safety with conscious victims
  ● lets you conserve energy, given the water conditions and the distance to safety.

Once you've chosen a carry, adapt it as necessary to suit *yourself*. For example, if you have short arms for your height, you may want to adapt one or more carries to make them more effective.

You might want to *change* from one carry to another. You might be tired, the victim's condition might have changed, the water conditions might have changed, etc. Maintain full support and control of the victim *throughout the change-over*. With conscious victims, explain what you will be doing, why it must be done, and how you will do it. Don't change carries until you *and* the victim are ready for it.

4.12   Removals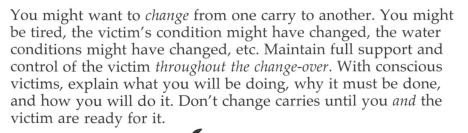

Remove victims from the water as soon as possible, and use the removal method with the least risk *for you and the victim*.

Here are some *general* tips on removal from the water:
- ❏ When using vertical lifts, ask for assistance whenever help is needed. Bystanders can be directed both to support victims and to help during the removal.
- ❏ In single-rescuer methods, take care to ensure *everyone's* safety: the victim's *and* yours.
- ❏ Removing wet, heavy victims from the water can be hard if they can't help themselves or are injured. You risk injury, especially to the back, if you don't use safe lifting techniques (see sidebar).
- ❏ Always think of the victim being removed. Be sure you have full control of the victim in all lifting and removal techniques. Avoid any movements that pull or twist victims' joints.

> **Principles of Safe Lifting**
> ✓ Use your legs, not your back.
> ✓ Bring the person you are lifting as close to your body as possible.
> ✓ Avoid twisting motions.
> ✓ Use smooth, controlled movements.

Possible Removal Methods
- ❏ Underarm lift
- ❏ Cradle lift
- ❏ Walk out
- ❏ One-rescuer drag
- ❏ Firefighter's carry
- ❏ Over-one-shoulder carry

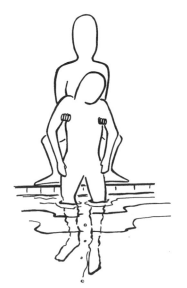

Underarm Lift
This removal works well for removing a victim to a deck or dock:
- ✓ Hold the victim in a stable position in which he or she faces away from you.
- ✓ Reach from behind, and hold the victim securely *under* the armpits. Place your hands securely on the victim's chest.
- ✓ Lift the victim vertically until he or she is above the surface you're standing on (deck, dock, etc.). Make sure you don't scrape the victim's back.
- ✓ Step back gently, and lower the victim to a secure sitting position on the surface you're standing on. The victim should be far enough from the edge that he or she can't fall back into the water.

If the victim is unconscious, a second rescuer can be very helpful. This rescuer does NOT have to be a trained lifesaver. To remove an unconscious victim when there is no bystander to help, modify the underarm lift as follows:

✓ Reach past the armpits, and hold the victim's wrists.

✓ Make sure the victim's elbows are pointing down (not out) and your arms are pointing forward, not down. These precautions ensure that the victim is comfortable and that you lift safely.

The modified underarm lift is awkward to establish and requires more strength than the regular underarm lift.

✓ If a second rescuer is available, there are two options for removal. Here are the key points about each:

● The second rescuer is in front of the victim and in the water. Remember that the second rescuer need NOT be a trained lifesaver. With the victim in a sitting position, the second rescuer supports the victim's upper legs on his or her shoulder. On a signal they have agreed to, the rescuers lift *together* until the victim's back clears the deck, dock, etc.

● Both rescuers are on the same surface (deck, dock, etc.), and the victim's back is to them. Each rescuer grabs one of the victim's armpits from behind. On a signal they have agreed to, the rescuers lift *together* and pull the victim away from the edge of the surface. The rescuers take care not to scrape the victim's back.

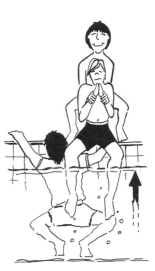

> ### Removals with Two or More Rescuers
> ✓ When more than one rescuer is involved, teamwork is essential for a smooth removal. Agree on a signal, for example, "Lift on a count of 3. 1. . .2. . .3."
> ✓ Rescuers must grasp each other's hands firmly:
> ● With your fingers together, curl your fingers toward your palms.
> ● Have the other rescuer do the same thing.
> ● You can "hook" your fingers together in a hold that wrestlers use. It's comfortable and doesn't break easily.
> ● Avoid gripping each other's wrists or using a handshake grip — they both slip when wet.

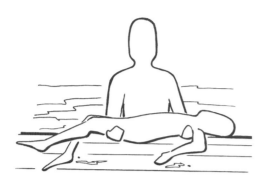

Cradle Lift

This removal works best for removing victims from shallow water to a dock or deck:
- ✓ The victim is at the surface, cradled in your outstretched arms and parallel to the lip or edge of a pool, deck, dock, etc.
- ✓ Hook one arm under the victim's thighs and the other under his or her neck.
- ✓ Lift the victim, and place him or her *gently* on the deck, dock, etc.

Unless the victim is *much* smaller than you, DON'T do this removal alone.

If a second rescuer or bystander is available, modify the cradle lift as follows:
- ✓ Rescuer 1 holds the victim as in the cradle lift described above.
- ✓ Rescuer 2 or bystander crouches on the deck or dock and crosses his or her arms.
- ✓ Rescuer 2 grasps Rescuer 1's right hand with his or her right hand, Rescuer 1's left hand with his or her left hand.
- ✓ On an agreed-upon signal, both rescuers stand up. Rescuer 2 steps back from the edge, moving the victim into position on the deck or dock.

Walk Out

This removal is especially useful at a beach or in other open-water situations:
- ✓ If the victim is conscious and exhausted and you're both in shallow water, pause there briefly.
- ✓ Supporting the victim, walk out of the water. Put one arm around the victim's waist; the victim's arm is over your shoulder.

One-Rescuer Drag

This technique is useful if you are alone, the victim is unconscious, and you need to move him or her a short distance *fast*. It is also useful at a beach or in other open-water situations:

- ✓ From behind the victim, reach under his or her armpits, and grab his or her wrists.
- ✓ Pull the victim out of the water, heels dragging.
- ✓ Place the victim in a position suitable for treatment.

Firefighter's Carry

This removal requires either a small-sized victim or a rescuer with a high level of strength and power. It is quite useful at a beach or in other open-water situations. This is a useful removal method when you're alone:

✓ In shallow water, face the victim.

✓ Pick up the victim in one of two ways:

● Grab the victim's nearer upper arm with one hand. Place your other hand on the inside of the victim's nearer leg and just above the knee. Submerge beneath the victim in a squatting position, keeping your chin tucked close to your chest. Roll the victim over, and stand up with the victim draped over your shoulders as you do so. With one hand, clasp the victim's lower arm and lower leg against your body. Balance with the other hand while walking to shore.

● Kneel down, and draw one of the victim's arms across your shoulders. Slip your own arm between the victim's legs. As you turn your back to the victim, support him or her across your shoulders.

✓ To put the victim down,

● bend your knees and hips, allowing the victim's feet to touch the ground.

● holding the victim on your shoulders, turn from the hip to grasp the victim around the chest with both hands.

● once the victim is supported, lower him or her gently to the ground. Protect the victim's head as you do this.

With practice, you will know when to start this carry to ensure that the victim's head is always clear of the water.

Over-One-Shoulder Carry

This removal requires either a small-sized victim or a rescuer with a high level of strength and power. It is quite useful at a beach or in other open-water situations. This carry is used when *no* help is available:

✓ Lift the victim over one of your shoulders so that he or she pikes at the waist.

✓ Grasp the victim's dangling legs.

✓ Transport the victim to safety *slowly* and *deliberately*. (Walking hurriedly can cause victims to vomit, especially if they've eaten recently or swallowed water during their near-drowning.)

Choosing a Removal Method

When choosing a removal method, consider

❏ the victim's condition

❏ the availability of assistance

❏ your abilities

❏ characteristics of the removal site, for example, water depth, water conditions, and the height of the deck, dock, or shoreline.

4.13   Follow-up ✔

Once the victim has been removed from the water, evaluate his or her condition, and start follow-up procedures. If possible, get help moving the victim to a more comfortable environment (see page 4-2 for how to use bystanders in a rescue). Call EMS if necessary, and decide whether the incident should be formally reported to an authority.

The drowning process may result in Acute Respiratory Distress some hours after the initial drowning event and rescue. After rescue from the water, the victim should be sent to hospital if he or she:

✓ suffered any loss of consciousness

✓ required resuscitation (rescue breathing, CPR)

✓ has any concurrent condition (e.g. seizure, spinal injury, asthma)

After the rescue is over, *evaluate* your experience, and learn from it. Go over the rescue from beginning to end. Review every element in the rescue process (see page 4-2), and ask yourself questions like these:

❏ *Recognize*. How accurately and how fast did you recognize the victim's condition?

❏ *Assess*. How effective was your assessment? Did you choose the safest rescue possible? Did you change your assessment as conditions changed?

❏ *Act*. How well did you perform the lifesaving skills you chose? How and why did this incident happen? What could prevent such incidents in the future?

For the Assess element of the rescue process, use the Ladder Approach as your evaluation tool; for the Act element, use the Rescuer's Checklist.

When you do your evaluation, be honest and realistic. By being honest with yourself about what you did and didn't do well, you'll become a better rescuer. By being realistic, you'll set reasonable standards for yourself in future rescues.

4.14   Want to Know More?

Huint, Richard. *Understanding Drowning (and Related Topics)*. Montreal: AquaLude Inc., 1992.

> This text presents detailed information on the physiology of drowning and summarizes significant scientific research on the subject. It is of particular interest to lifeguards and aquatics instructors.

Pia, Frank. *On Drowning*. Frank Pia: 1992. (Available from Water Safety Films Inc., Larchmont, New York.)

> This video features footage of actual near-drownings and rescues at a New York beach. Also included in the film are Frank Pia's discussions of distressed swimmers and drowning research.

Lifesaving Society. *Alert: Lifeguarding in Action*. Ottawa: Royal Life Saving Society Canada, 1993.

> *Alert* is the text of the National Lifeguard Service. Designed for professional lifeguards, *Alert* presents information on accident prevention and rescue skills and procedures.

Chapter 5
Specialized Lifesaving Skills

5.1   Introduction

Chapter 4 described the fundamental skills needed to perform safe, effective, and efficient rescues of others. Those key skills make up the rescue process, and they're *usually* all you need to use in a rescue.

But sometimes these basic skills aren't enough. For example, the person you're rescuing might grab you—and put *your* life in danger. Or a drowning victim could have a spinal injury, and this requires specialized treatment skills.

This chapter covers the following specialized lifesaving skills:
- ❑ avoidance
- ❑ defences
- ❑ releases
- ❑ searches for missing persons
- ❑ using skin-diving equipment
- ❑ ice rescue
- ❑ multiple-victim rescues
- ❑ multiple-rescuer procedures
- ❑ rescue procedures for spinal injuries
- ❑ rescue breathing in deep water.

**Stride entry using
skin-diving equipment**

5.2 Avoidance

Avoidance is a primary goal for *all* rescuers. With distressed swimmers and drowning victims, you need to minimize the risk of being grabbed during a rescue. Here are some tips on how to *avoid* victims to ensure your own safety:

✓ Watch the victim.
✓ Be attentive to the victim's body movements and intentions.
✓ Be watchful about the possibility of being grabbed.
✓ Use the Ladder Approach to choose the safest rescue method, given the situation (see pages 4-4 to 4-9 for information on the Ladder Approach).
✓ If the victim tries to grab you, either swim away or submerge (see below for information on defences).
✓ Resume a ready position.
✓ Talk to the victim to explain that he or she mustn't try to hold onto you.
✓ Repeat the rescue approach *if and when you and the victim are ready.*

Rescuer in ready position

5.3 Defences

You may need to use defences to avoid contact with victims in certain situations. A rescue may not go as planned, or you may be taken by surprise. For instance, in a boating accident, you and others might suddenly find yourself within a victim's grasp.

Whenever you have to use a defence,
✓ move away quickly
✓ resume a ready position
✓ talk to the victim to explain that he or she mustn't hold onto you
✓ repeat the rescue approach *if and when you and the victim are ready.*

Choose defences on the basis of where the victim is relative to you when he or she approaches. Here are the defences you need to know:
❏ duck away from the front
❏ duck away from the rear
❏ foot block
❏ arm block.

Duck away from the Front

✓ Move away from the victim, submerging as quickly as possible and avoiding all contact.
✓ A modified foot-first surface dive, in which there is no upward scissor kick, is usually the quickest technique to use to submerge.
✓ Orient yourself and the victim so that you can swim underwater to a safe distance from the victim.
✓ Stay in the reverse and ready position as you surface.

Duck away from the Rear

If you sense the victim approaching from behind you,
✓ submerge to get away
✓ orient yourself and the victim so that you can swim underwater to a safe distance from the victim
✓ stay in the reverse and ready position as you surface.

Duck away from front

Foot Block

Use the foot block to push away a victim who moves toward you when you're in the foot-first ready position:
✓ Place one foot against the victim's upper chest or shoulder.
✓ Extend the leg to push the victim away.
✓ Return to the reverse and ready position, and make sure there's enough distance between you and the victim.

Arm Block

✓ Extend one arm, and press forcefully against the victim's upper body to move away.
✓ This is the highest risk block, and *you should avoid it if at all possible.*
✓ Return to the reverse and ready position, and make sure there's enough distance between you and the victim.

Duck away from rear

Foot block   **Arm block**

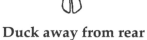

5.4   Releases

You may be grabbed by a victim during a rescue. This might happen if the victim's condition changes (getting tired or confused, for example) or if you don't plan effectively for your own safety. Because of panic, the intensity of the victim's strength and power are often intensified. Releases can be used in such situations.

It is *not at all certain* that releases will succeed if a victim grabs you. That's why this section does not include specific release techniques—it could give the impression there are sequential steps to success in such situations. Instead, release *principles* are listed, with the warning they are *guidelines* for these potentially life-threatening situations.

Release Principles

If you *have* to use a release, remember the following:
- ❏ This is a life-threatening situation for you.
- ❏ Submerge the victim if possible.
- ❏ The next option is to submerge yourself *and* the victim if he or she is still holding onto you.
- ❏ Try to use quick, high-velocity movements.
- ❏ Orient yourself to water surface and depth. Resurface in the reverse and ready position a safe distance from the victim.
- ❏ If you are grabbed around the neck, tuck your chin.
- ❏ Do *not* further endanger yourself. Consider a low-risk rescue, and remember self-rescue principles.

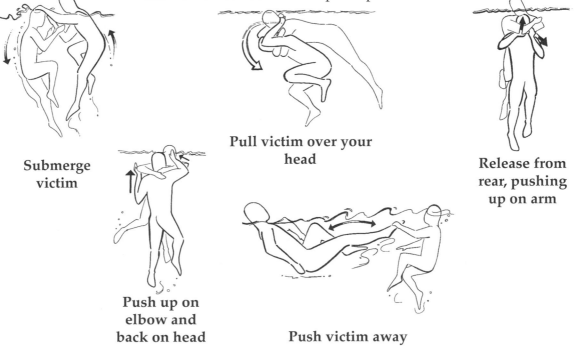

Submerge victim

Pull victim over your head

Release from rear, pushing up on arm

Push up on elbow and back on head

Push victim away

5.5   Searches for Missing Persons

Searches must be started when
✓ a missing person is believed to be in the water
✓ a person is known to have submerged and his or her exact
location is unknown.

If a missing person is not *known* to be in the water, both land
and water searches are required.

Searches in Shallow Water
✓ Shallow-water areas are best searched by a team
that walks through the area in a straight line with
hands joined.
✓ If the water is murky, the team needs to close up
the space between each searcher and rely on what
searchers feel, not on what they see.
✓ One person should be the leader, directing search
participants and other bystanders, ensuring that
the entire area is covered, and co-ordinating the
line's speed of movement.
✓ If you're alone, call for help while scanning the
area from shore. If you can't see the victim, wade
out to the farthest point necessary, and walk back and forth
in lines parallel to shore, moving closer to shore on each
sweep. Use reference points on land to ensure that the entire
water area is covered.

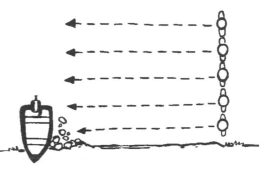

**Group search, overhead view, using
boat and rocks as reference points**

Searches in Deep Water
✓ Whenever possible, deep-water searches should be
conducted by two or more people using a series of surface
dives and a systematic pattern to cover the area.
✓ Always swim in straight lines underwater, and turn
corners only at the surface. This helps you
determine what area has been covered.
✓ Use land markings to develop a grid
pattern and determine the area to cover
underwater. The width of the grid pattern
will depend on water clarity—the better
the clarity, the farther you can see, and the
wider the grid pattern can be.
✓ Searchers should be able to easily see one
another underwater.
✓ The depth of the search will depend on the
clarity of water. Searchers need to swim
at a depth where they can clearly see the
bottom.

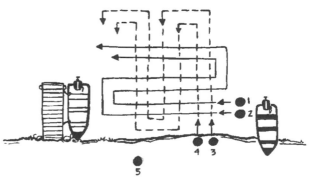

**Landmarking and grid pattern,
overhead view**

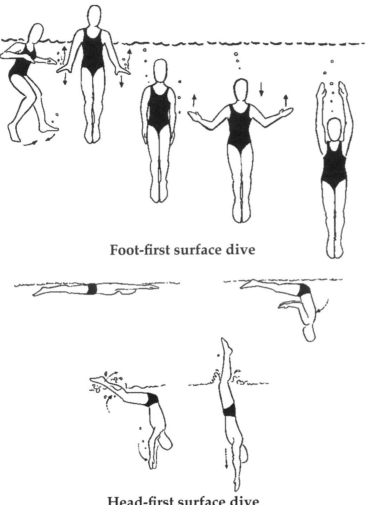

Foot-first surface dive

Head-first surface dive

✓ Foot-first surface dives are recommended for underwater searches. These dives protect the rescuer's head if there are underwater hazards. (See pages 9-14 and 9-15 for more information on these dives.)

✓ Searchers who decide to do a head-first surface dive *must back up before submerging* to ensure they cover the entire area.

✓ Rescuers should surface frequently to avoid getting tired. Searchers tire quickly if they try to cover too large an area all at once.

✓ If there are three or more rescuers and the victim is *not* known to be in the water, one person should conduct a land search while the best swimmers conduct a water search.

✓ Skin-diving equipment can increase the efficiency of underwater searches (Section 5.6 describes this equipment and its use).

Searches in Swimming Pools

✓ Clear the pool of all swimmers *before starting a search*.

✓ Investigate all unidentifiable shadows or objects on the bottom of the pool.

✓ Search swimming pools with a visual scan from the deck or a higher vantage point. Pay special attention to the corners and to the bottom drains.

✓ If it is not *known* that the victim is in the pool, two rescuers should scan the water while other rescuers start a search of shower rooms, locker rooms, and all other possible areas (including lockers).

✓ If the water being searched is cloudy, use the techniques presented above for deep-water searches.

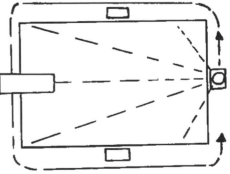

5.6   Using Skin-Diving Equipment

Skin-diving equipment increases the efficiency of underwater searches:
- ❏ Face masks provide clear vision. This makes it possible for each rescuer to search a greater area than he or she could without a mask.
- ❏ Snorkels allow you to concentrate *completely* on the search, because you don't have to lift your head to breathe.
- ❏ Fins increase propulsion and reduce the swimming effort required. With fins, you don't have to use your hands for propulsion.

Face Masks
To test a face mask for proper fit, hold it in place, and inhale through the nose. When you remove your hand, the mask should stay in position on your face.

One of the first skills to learn is how to clear the mask when it fills with water. There are three ways to do this, and each involves displacing water by exhaling through the nose. The three methods are
- ❏ doing a horizontal roll
- ❏ doing a vertical tilt
- ❏ using the mask's purge valve.

Testing for proper fit

Doing a Horizontal Roll
When you are swimming or searching, the horizontal roll is more useful for clearing the mask than the vertical tilt.
- ✓ Get into a horizontal position, and press one side of the mask firmly against your face.
- ✓ Blow air through your nose while rolling onto the opposite side to displace water out the lower side of the mask. (The mask should be clear as you complete your roll.)
- ✓ Use a *minimum* of exhaled air to clear the mask—you also have to exhale to clear the snorkel.

Horizontal roll

Doing a Vertical Tilt
- ✓ Get into a position in which your upper body is vertical in the water.
- ✓ Press the top part of the mask firmly against your forehead.
- ✓ Exhale slowly and steadily through the nose, tilting your head back to about a 45° angle to the surface.

Vertical tilt

Using the Mask's Purge Valve
✓ Move your head so that the purge valve is the lowest part of the mask in the water.
✓ Press the mask firmly against your face as you exhale through your nose, forcing water out through the valve.
✓ Keep your head in the same position *throughout*.

The design of purge valves varies from model to model. *Practise* to discover the best method for the model you're likely to use.

> ### Facts about Face Masks
> ❑ Water vapor may form on the inside of the lens. You can prevent this from happening by applying an anti-fog compound to the inside surface of the lens.
> ❑ The deeper you submerge, the more pressure there is against your face. You can equalize this pressure by exhaling a small amount of air through your nose.

Snorkels

Snorkels are hollow plastic tubes with a flexible rubber mouthpiece. Divers attach snorkels to the side of their mask. Divers bite on two protrusions; the flange of the mouthpiece rests between the teeth and the inside of the lips.

When you submerge, the snorkel partially fills with water. To clear the snorkel at the surface, exhale a quick, sharp puff of air that forces water out of the tube.

To inhale immediately after surfacing,
✓ ascend vertically with your head tilted slightly back so that the tip of the snorkel is lower than the mouthpiece (look toward the water surface).
✓ blow into the snorkel while still submerged. This displaces the water in the tube, and the tube should be clear by the time you reach the surface.

With practice, you can learn to clear your mask and your snorkel with one breath.

Fins

Fins are easier to put on if your feet are wet. Here are some tips on choosing fins:
❑ It's important that fins *fit your feet*. Fins that are too large cause sores and blisters; fins that are too tight can cause poor blood circulation and even muscle cramps.
❑ Fins should be rigid enough to stay still during downward leg movement.
❑ The larger the surface area, the more energy it takes to kick.
❑ Fins with an inclined blade provide maximum propulsion.

You use two basic kicks with fins—a flutter kick and a dolphin kick:
❑ The leg action of the flutter kick is slower than that used in the crawl. The kick is initiated from the hips, and the fins stay submerged.

Flutter kick

❏ In the dolphin kick, the legs move together, with the knees and hips flexing and then extending in the drive phase. The leg action is slow and relaxed.

When swimming underwater with fins, keep one or both arms extended directly in front of you—it streamlines your body, minimizes resistance, and provides extra protection for your face.

Dolphin kick

Entering the Water with Skin-Diving Equipment

Entering Shallow Water from a Beach
✓ Enter by walking backward (it's easier than walking forward when you're wearing fins).
✓ Take care not to trip or slip.
✓ Start to swim when you reach deep enough water.

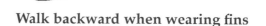

Walk backward when wearing fins

Entering with a Forward Roll
✓ Using one or both hands to hold the mask and snorkel in position, roll forward in a pike position.
✓ Keep your chin tucked, and enter the water with your shoulders and neck leading and your feet together.

Forward roll entry

Entering with a Back-Sit Entry
✓ Use one or both hands to hold the mask and snorkel in position.
✓ With your back to the water, fall backward into a V-sit position.
✓ The buttocks and lower back strike the water first.
✓ Do this entry *only from a limited height* (a small boat, for instance).

Back-sit entry

Entering with a Stride Jump
Your head does *not* submerge in this entry:

✓ Take a wide stride.
✓ Enter the water feet first.
✓ Use your hands and chest to resist downward momentum.

Precautions for Scuba Diving and Skin Diving
Preventing Squeezes
❑ Practise scuba diving or skin diving only if you are in good physical and dental health.
❑ Avoid diving with a cold or breathing problem.
❑ Avoid using decongestants or other medication before dives.
❑ Equalize pressure early and often by pinching the nose, closing the mouth, and blowing gently from the throat. Do not wait to feel pain in your ears to do this.

Preventing Air Embolism
❑ Breathe regularly—avoid breath holding.
❑ Ascend slowly—no faster than 20 metres per minute.

Preventing Decompression Sickness
❑ Use decompression tables when scuba diving. They help you adjust to the pressure at different depths.
❑ If possible, avoid things that reduce blood flow: alcohol, extreme fatigue, extremely hot or cold showers, dehydration, obesity, etc.
❑ Follow the bubbles when ascending—no faster than 20 metres per minute.

5.7   Ice Rescue

When a person falls through thin ice, you must understand that the same thing can happen to you if you approach the area of the hole. You can help victims *only from a distance*:

✓ Anyone on or near the weak ice should *immediately* but *slowly* get low to the ground and distribute his or her weight over as large an area as possible. This could involve crawling, for example, or moving commando-style on the stomach.

✓ Use a long assist: a ring buoy with a rope, a rope or hose, a long stick, a ladder, etc.

✓ When the victim grasps the assist, pull gently to help him or her *ease* out of the water.

✓ Advise the victim to ease along the ice, distributing his or her weight as much as possible until it's safe to do otherwise. In many situations, it's best to *crawl* along the ice with the feet spread.

✓ As soon as you can approach the victim, help him or her to safety. Wet clothing can then be removed.

✓ Assess the victim's condition, looking especially for signs or symptoms of hypothermia (see page 8-24). Provide any necessary treatment and follow-up care. This can include sending the victim to hospital.

5.8   Multiple-Victim Rescues

Some rescues involve more than one victim. For example, a boat may swamp or capsize unexpectedly, a weak swimmer may grab another swimmer for support, or a current may carry swimmers into deep water.

Rescuing more than one victim at the same time is hard. It also requires advanced lifesaving judgment, knowledge, skill, and fitness. As a lifesaver, you need to understand the risks involved in such rescues.

Here are the basic *principles* of multiple-victim rescues:

✓ If possible, take two or more assists, and tow the victims to shore. This may involve towing two or more victims at the same time.

✓ If a boat is involved, have victims cling to it or to an attached rope, ladder, etc., and transport the victims to safety. If the boat is very small, transport victims one or two at a time in order of the seriousness of their condition.

> In any rescue, treat the victim as an individual. Take into account factors such as his or her abilities (including physical or learning disabilities). Modify techniques as necessary.

Towing or Carrying Two Victims

✓ If you have two assists or if both victims can hold one assist, you can tow both victims to safety at the same time.

✓ If both victims stay calm, try to get them on their backs, side by side.

✓ Swim in front of and between the two victims, pulling them to safety with an assist.

✓ If you *have* to use a carry, use the safest one possible, and pull the victims to safety. If the victims are calm, ask one to hold the feet of the other during your carry. If you're strong and the water is calm, you might be able to carry two victims this way for a short distance. If you *can't* do this, tell the victim in the carry to hold the other victim under his or her arms.

5.9   Multiple-Rescuer Procedures

When there's more than one rescuer, having a *leader* ensures both the best teamwork *and* the fastest rescue of the victim. Trained rescuers should be prepared to assume this leadership role in *any* situation involving more than one rescuer. This is especially important when the rescuer has recruited untrained assistants. Trained rescuers should

✓ recruit bystanders to assist in the rescue (see page 4-2)

✓ give clear, specific direction to assistants

✓ ensure ongoing communication among everyone participating in the rescue

✓ quickly determine the swimming skills of individuals recruited to assist in the water.

When there's more than one rescuer, one might be directly involved in the rescue while others get first aid supplies, call EMS, etc. If there are two rescuers and both *are* involved in the rescue, there are many ways they can team up on the tow or carry. Here are just a few examples:

✓ Rescuer 1 carries the victim while Rescuer 2 carries Rescuer 1.

✓ Rescuers 1 and 2 both carry the victim, one on each side.

✓ Rescuer 1 carries the victim while Rescuer 2 assesses the victim's condition.

✓ Rescuer 1 carries the victim while Rescuer 2 immobilizes an injured body part.

5.10   Rescue Procedures for Spinal Injuries

While injuries to the head and spine account for a small percentage of all injuries, they represent a large number of serious injuries and deaths. Injuries to the head and spine can damage both bone (skull, vertebrae) and soft tissue (brain, spinal cord, nerves). Prompt care can prevent further damage to some head and spine injuries. (See pages 8-12 and 8-13 for more information on the treatment of spinal injuries.)

Proper treatment of a victim with spinal injuries requires the co-ordination of many skills into a sequence that
❏ immobilizes the spine
❏ maintains the airway, breathing, and circulation
❏ allows for removal and transportation to hospital or other medical facility.

Rescuers must use judgment in deciding how and when to stabilize a victim using a rollover and when to use a spinal board. Factors to consider when making these decisions include the number of rescuers available, the victim's condition, and the water and weather conditions.

The essential tasks in spinal rescues focus on the following:
❏ contacting EMS
❏ approach
❏ rollover and immobilization
❏ ABCs (airway, breathing, and circulation)
❏ stabilization and spinal board
❏ removal
❏ treatment for shock
❏ further treatment.

While the ABCs are listed fourth in the sequence, *they are still the priority*. This means you must do the first three steps efficiently so that the ABC priorities can be assessed, treated, and monitored.

Contacting EMS
✓ Send a second rescuer or bystander to contact EMS and return with an AED if available.
✓ If you are alone, contact EMS and get an AED (if one is immediately available) before initiating the spinal rescue.
✓ For more information about contacting EMS, see page 3-3.

> AED stands for Automated External Defibrillation. An AED unit is an Automated External Defibrillator. (See sidebar on page 7-13).

Approach

✓ Slip into the water.
✓ Approach the victim carefully to minimize water movement.
✓ Do *not* jump or dive into the water near the victim.

Rollover and Immobilization

When the victim is on his or her back or floating with the head up, a rollover is *not* needed. If the victim is face down or partially submerged, you may need to roll him or her over to assess and maintain the ABCs and immobilize the head and neck.

Rollover and immobilization techniques involve the alignment or realignment of the head in the neutral position (the nose is in a straight line with the belly button).

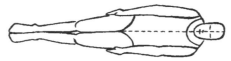

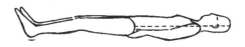

In the following cases, however, you should NOT move the victim's head in line with the body:

❏ if you feel resistance when trying to move the head
❏ if the victim complains of pain-like pressure or muscle spasms when you first try to move the head
❏ if the victim's head is severely angled.

In these cases, support the victim's head in the position you found it.

There are many rollover and immobilization techniques to choose from (three basic techniques are described in detail below). Choose and modify as necessary *any* technique that meets *all* of the following criteria:

✓ The required number of trained rescuers is available.
✓ The technique reduces or prevents movement of the victim's head and neck.
✓ The technique allows you to assess and monitor the ABCs.
✓ The technique allows you to do rescue breathing.
✓ The technique allows you to hold the victim's body at or just below the surface.

Canadian Rollover and Immobilization Technique

This technique is useful when the victim is in very shallow water, the victim is much smaller than the rescuer (for example, an adult rescuer and a child victim), or there are few trained rescuers (one, two, or three rescuers). In the Canadian rollover, the victim's head and neck are splinted between his or her extended arms. This technique may not be suitable for victims with bulky, muscular shoulders, because the extended arms may not be able to squeeze the victim's head.

Technique is as follows:
- ✓ Stand on either side of the victim.
- ✓ Grasp the victim's arms midway between the elbow and the shoulder — your right hand on the victim's right arm, your left hand on the victim's left arm.
- ✓ Gently float the victim's arms up alongside his or her head, parallel to the water surface.
- ✓ Position the victim's arms so that they extend against his or her head.
- ✓ Apply pressure to the arms with your fingers while placing your thumbs on the back of the victim's head to eliminate back-and-forth movement of his or her head.
- ✓ Lower your body to chest depth, and move the victim slowly forward and to a horizontal position, gliding the victim's body to the surface.
- ✓ As the victim becomes horizontal in the water, keep moving forward slowly and rotating the victim toward you until he or she is face up.
- ✓ Rest the victim's head in the crook of your arm.
- ✓ Assess the victim's breathing.

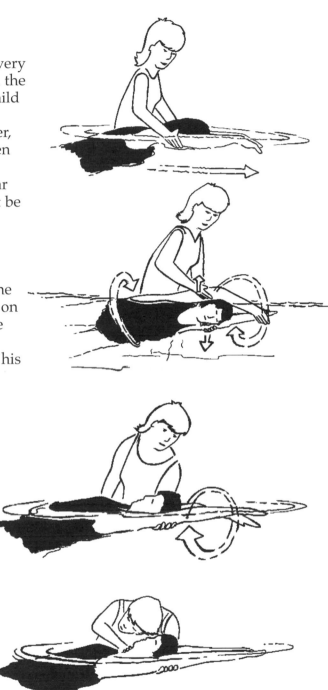

Vice Grip Rollover and Immobilization Technique

This technique is useful when there are few trained rescuers (one, two, or three rescuers). In the vice grip, the victim is sandwiched front to back between the rescuer's forearms. When there is only one rescuer and he or she is much smaller than the victim, it may be difficult or even impossible to assess the ABCs and perform rescue breathing using this technique.

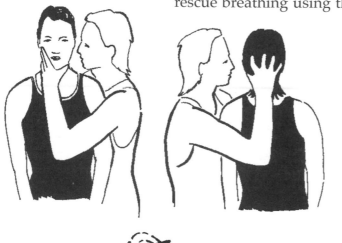

Technique is as follows:

✓ Stand beside the victim, and face his or her head.
✓ Lower your body until your shoulders are at water level.
✓ Reaching into the water with one arm, place your forearm along his or her sternum. Place your other forearm along the spine.
✓ The hand in front supports the chin; the thumb is on one side, the fingers on the other.
✓ At the same time, use the other hand to support the victim's neck at the base of the skull. To do this, spread the fingers, and cradle the head.
✓ Lock both your wrists, squeeze your forearms together, and clamp the victim's chest and back between your forearms and hands.
✓ Turn the victim face up by keeping your hands in position and rotating the victim toward you while you start to lower yourself in the water.
✓ Carefully roll under the victim while turning him or her over in the water. The victim is face up when stabilized. Move slowly to avoid *any* twisting of the victim's body.

Modified Body Rollover and Immobilization Technique

This technique should be used only if there are at least two *trained* rescuers — otherwise, the ABCs cannot be assessed or monitored during rollover and immobilization.

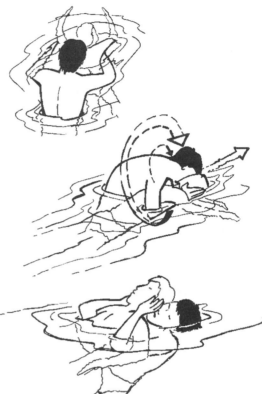

Technique is as follows:
- ✓ Stand beside the victim, facing his or her head.
- ✓ Place your hands between the victim's arms and torso.
- ✓ Reach in front of the victim's shoulders with your hands (your right hand to the victim's right shoulder, your left hand to the victim's left shoulder).
- ✓ *Gently* move your arms forward until your hands reach the sides of the victim's head. Your hands are open with the thumb behind the ear and the fingers in front. The base of each hand is along the jawline. *Do not apply pressure yet.*
- ✓ Squeeze your elbows into the victim's body, and then apply pressure with your forearms and hands.
- ✓ Lower your body, and place your head beside the victim.
- ✓ Turn the victim face up, keeping your hands in position on either side of the head with your elbows secured. Rotate the victim toward you while you submerge yourself.
- ✓ Carefully roll under the victim while turning him or her over in the water. Both you and the victim are face up when you surface on the other side.
- ✓ Move slowly to avoid twisting the victim's body.
- ✓ The second rescuer assesses and monitors breathing and circulation.

Spinal Injuries in Deep Water

People rarely suffer spinal injuries in deep water. But if this does happen, you will need to do one of the following:
- ✓ Move yourself and the victim to shallow water after the rollover and immobilization by doing a lifesaving kick. Eggbeater is the kick of choice, because it involves the least water movement around the victim.
- ✓ If you can't move to shallow water, secure the victim to the edge of the dock, pool, boat, or other stable object.
- ✓ The final choice would be to straddle an assist such as a rescue tube to provide buoyancy.

ABCs

Checking for breathing does not always require rolling the victim onto his or her back. A cry of pain, chest movement, or the sound of breathing tells you the victim is breathing. Here are the key points about the ABCs as they relate to spinal injuries (for a detailed description of the ABCs, see Chapter 7).

Airway

While airway is always a high priority, you need to modify what you do when you suspect a spinal injury:

✓ If the victim is breathing, monitor breathing closely.

✓ To assess the airway or to perform rescue breaths, attempt to open the airway using a jaw thrust technique. If the jaw thrust does not work (i.e., rescue breaths do not go in), use the head-tilt/chin-lift technique.

Jaw Thrust Technique.

✓ Place your hands on each side of the victim's head with 2 or 3 fingers positioned behind the angle of the jaw.

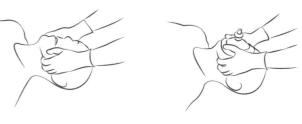

✓ Place your thumbs on the cheek bones and thrust the jaw upward without moving the neck.

✓ Unless using a pocket mask, seal the victim's nose with the thumbs or cheek while performing rescue breaths.

Head-Tilt/Chin-Lift Technique. If the victim is an adult,

✓ place one hand on the victim's forehead, and apply firm backward (downward) pressure with the palm to tilt the head back.

✓ place the first two fingers of the other hand under the bony part of the lower jaw, near the chin. Lift to bring the chin forward (upward) and almost close the teeth. If you are using a rescue breathing pocket mask, you may find that you can also lift the chin by hooking your fingers under the angle of the jaw and gently lifting the jaw up.

If the victim is a child or infant,

✓ be careful not to hyperextend the neck.

Breathing

✓ Perform a quick, visual check (5 sec.) for absent or abnormal breathing. Look for chest movement and listen for breathing. Abnormal breathing can include noisy and gasping (agonal) breaths.

See pages 7-10 to 7-12 for a full description of how to do rescue breathing.

Circulation

If the victim is breathing, assume effective circulation. If the victim is not breathing, or not breathing effectively (gasping), perform CPR. If the victim is found on land, start CPR with chest compressions. If found in the water, start with 2 rescue breaths.

Apply an AED (automated external defibrillator) as soon as it arrives.

✓ Remove the victim promptly to the pool deck or beach, and start CPR. If several rescuers and a spinal board are available (see below), quickly but carefully place the victim on a spinal board, and remove him or her immediately. Start CPR.

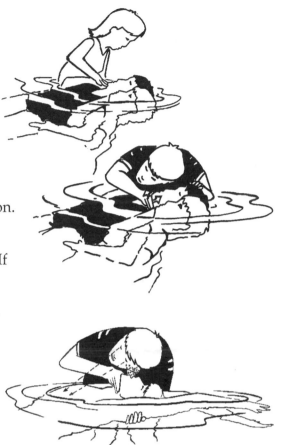

Stabilization and Spinal Board

This involves stabilizing the victim's hips, head, and neck and placing the victim on a spinal board *if enough rescuers and a spinal board are available.* Three or four rescuers are needed for effective stabilization. If the rescuers are lifeguards, one or two may be enough if there are bystanders who can help (see page 4-2 for information on what bystanders can do during a rescue).

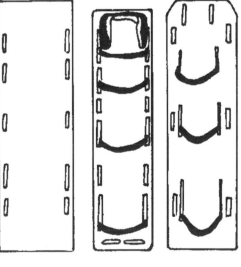

Lifeguards and advanced lifesavers should practise stabilization and removal to develop their skills in these techniques. See below for an example of spinal-board placement by two lifeguards.

A sample technique for stabilization is described below. Procedures will vary, depending on such factors as the victim's condition, rescuers' skill, the number of rescuers, and the equipment available. It is important to remember to check the ABCs at least once a minute throughout the stabilization procedure.

✓ Rescuer 1 has the victim immobilized and is checking and re-checking breathing.
✓ Rescuer 2 moves to hold the victim's hips and thighs up.
✓ Rescuer 3 holds the victim's feet up.

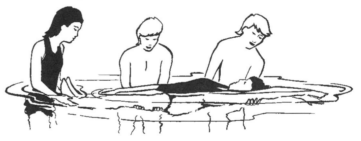

✓ Rescuer 4 brings the spinal board into the water and approaches the victim from the side.

✓ Rescuer 4 holds the board under the water so that it doesn't bump the victim. He or she then slides the board under the victim and positions it lengthwise along the victim's spine.
✓ The board is allowed to rise under the victim.

✓ Rescuer 3 places a hand on each side of the victim's head to help minimize movement as Rescuer 1 slowly and carefully withdraws his or her hands from the victim's head.

✓ Rescuers 1 and 4 secure chest straps snugly under the victim's armpits.

✓ Hip straps are secured with the victim's arms at his or her sides.

✓ The victim's head is secured on both sides. If the board has a head harness, it is used. Sandbags, rolled towels, etc., may also be used. The head should not be moved while being secured.

✓ All remaining straps are secured at the thighs and feet.

Alternative Immobilization Techniques

Several techniques can be used for immobilization on land or to maintain immobilization in the water while transferring a spinal-injured victim onto a spinal board. The techniques described below allow a spinal board to be positioned without interference because the rescuer's arm is not under the victim.

Trapezius Squeeze

✓ usually used to transfer from the vice grip or modified body

✓ place your hands and forearms alongside the victim's ears

✓ place your tumbs on the victim's collarbone or trapezius muscle and your fingers below the shoulders

✓ squeeze your forearms together to splint the head and neck

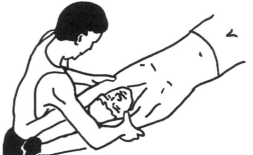

Reverse Canadian
- ✓ usually used to transfer from the Canadian immobilization technique
- ✓ grasp the victim's arms as close to the ears as possible
- ✓ gently squeeze the victim's arms together to maintain the immobilization

Removal

Whenever possible, a person with a suspected spinal injury should be removed from shallow water. Removal requires at least two rescuers if a spinal board is involved, and having three or four rescuers is preferred.

There are many techniques for removing victims from the water. But you risk injury, especially to the back, if you don't use safe lifting techniques (see page 4-24). *Any* removal procedure that allows for efficient, careful removal is appropriate. For example:
- ✓ Rescuers check that their grip is secure.
- ✓ If the victim is in a pool, the board is positioned at right angles to its side.
- ✓ The board is removed head-first.
- ✓ The board is kept horizontal for as long as possible while being removed.
- ✓ Bystanders can help by *smoothly* lifting and sliding the board.
- ✓ The rescuer at the victim's head should direct the removal by instructing all other rescuers to lift at an agreed-on signal. For instance, rescuers might agree to lift on the count of 3 in "1. . .2. . .3."

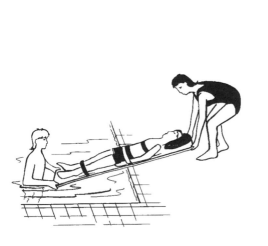

Treatment for Shock

Because a serious head or spinal injury can affect the body's heating and cooling mechanisms, victims with such injuries are quite susceptible to shock. See page 8-2 for information on how to treat shock.

Further Treatment

✓ Monitor vital signs.
✓ Do a secondary assessment, including a head-to-toe examination (see pages 6-5 to 6-7).
✓ Treat injuries.

5.11   Rescue Breathing in Deep Water

Rescue breathing in deep water is an option *for highly skilled rescuers* when the distance to shore, dock, or shallow water is too far to travel without ventilating the victim. You should use this lifesaving skill only when safer, less demanding procedures are not likely to save the victim. Deep-water rescue breathing can cause several problems for rescuers:

❑ Airway management is extremely difficult.
❑ Complications, such as vomiting, are difficult to handle in deep water.
❑ You and the victim lose body heat rapidly in the water. Because you and the victim travel more slowly during rescue breathing than during a control carry, the problem becomes more serious.

Deep-water rescue breathing requires a strong lifesaving kick. Because it provides continuous propulsion, eggbeater is most efficient. Be sure to pinch the victim's nose *continuously* during this rescue procedure. You can use any of the following techniques to support the victim:

✓ Support the victim with one hand under his or her neck and the other hand on his or her forehead. (This is like positioning the head for rescue breathing on land.) You may put your leg through a ring buoy or the armholes of a PFD or the neckhole of a lifejacket for additional support.
✓ Secure a rescue tube around the victim's torso, and support the head using one of the above techniques.

Modify these techniques according to your abilities, the victim's size, and the assists available. Whatever technique you use, maintain the airway, and ensure that water in the victim's face is minimal.

5.12   Want to Know More?

Pierce, Albert. *Scuba Life Saving*. Champaign, Illinois: Leisure Press, 1985.
> Produced by the Royal Life Saving Society Canada, this is a comprehensive guide to scuba safety and rescue techniques. The book goes beyond the basics, describing in detail the issues involved in real-life emergencies. Self-rescue techniques are covered, as are techniques involving one or more rescuers.

Lifesaving Society. *Alert: Lifeguarding in Action*. Ottawa: Royal Life Saving Society Canada, 1993.
> *Alert* is the text of the National Lifeguard Service. Designed for professional lifeguards, *Alert* presents information on accident prevention and rescue skills and procedures.

Lifesaving Society. *Ice: The Winter Killer: a resource manual about ice, ice safety and ice rescue*. Ottawa: Royal Life Saving Society Canada, 1998.
> Features ice-related drowning statistics; facts about ice, ice smart safety tips; signs and symptoms of cold shock response and hypothermia; ice rescue procedures; signs and symptoms of critical incident stress; steps to help communities promote ice safety.

Chapter 6
First Aid: The Rescue Process

6.1   Introduction

Lifesavers often say that first aid has three goals, which they call the 3 Ps:

✓ Preserve life.
✓ Prevent further injury.
✓ Promote recovery.

The first P is the most important. In first aid, you need to take care of life-threatening emergencies first. This chapter covers the rescue process for dealing with such emergencies. The elements in this process are as follows:

✓ Recognize.
✓ Assess.
✓ Act.

The rescue process is used in self-rescue, the rescue of others, and first aid. The three elements are the same in every type of rescue or first aid situation, but the element details are different. See Section 3.2 for how the process applies to self-rescue, Section 4.2 for how it applies to the rescue of others.

The following sections discuss the elements of the rescue process as they apply to first aid. Special attention is paid to the *assess* part of the rescue process.

6.2   First Aid: The Rescue Process

The rescue process applies to *all* first aid. You use it when first approaching a victim on land—for instance, when you find someone who's fainted from heat exhaustion. You use it when doing follow-up procedures in a water rescue, for example, treating a victim for shock. Whatever first aid emergency you deal with, *follow the rescue process.*

The rescue process is *dynamic*. You repeat its elements again and again until the victim has recovered or Emergency Medical System (EMS) personnel have taken over. In some cases, you will recognize-assess-act only once; in other cases, you will recognize-assess-act many times. Every emergency is different.

Recognize
✓ *Recognize* that the victim is in trouble and that help is needed.
✓ *Recognize* signs of danger to you at or near the emergency scene.

✓ *Recognize* clues about what happened to the victim.
✓ *Recognize* that aspects of the situation, such as the victim's condition, your condition, or the environment, may have changed.

Much of this recognizing happens *before* you reach the victim. Use all your senses as you approach him or her. Rely on what you feel, smell, and hear, not just on what you see.

Assess
There are four different assessments you *must* do in the rescue process. You must also do these assessments *in order*:
1 Assess the rescue environment, and remove hazards.
2 Conduct the primary assessment.
3 Get a history of the victim and the emergency.
4 Conduct the secondary assessment.

Remove hazards

Act
As a result of your assessment, you take action. Here are some of the actions you'll take:
✓ Treat the lifesaving priorities. (See Chapter 7 for a full description.)
✓ Treat other conditions. (See Chapter 8 for specific descriptions of signs, symptoms, and treatments.)
✓ Contact EMS if the victim's condition is serious or life-threatening (see page 3-3).

✓ Use bystanders where possible (see page 4-2).
✓ Transport the victim to safety if emergency services are not needed (see pages 4-20 to 4-24 for information on carries). This may mean moving the victim away from a hazard, removing him or her from the water, or taking him or her to the hospital.
✓ Contact the relevant authorities if the incident should be reported (see page 3-3).

6.3 Assess the Rescue Environment, and Remove Hazards

The rescue environment may involve dangers: live electrical wires, fire, extremely cold water, gas leaks, etc. If you think the environment could put you in danger, do NOT try to give first aid alone. Contact EMS instead. (See page 3-3 for information on how to contact such services.) If it is safe to do so, remove hazards from the rescue environment, or remove the victim from the hazardous area.

You must assess the environment even when you know you're not in immediate danger. Look for clues about what happened; a ladder that's fallen over, a nearby poison, or an electrical appliance may indicate the type and severity of the victim's injuries.

Assessments: Factors to Consider
During your assessments, you need to consider the following factors—each can affect your first aid efforts:
❑ victim priority. Some situations involve more than one victim. Always remember the ABC priorities (see Section 7.2), and focus on those most seriously injured. In such situations, do a primary assessment on all victims, and contact the Emergency Medical System (EMS) if necessary. Go on to a secondary assessment only after you're sure you've dealt with the ABC priorities for all victims.
❑ changes in the victim's condition or in the environment. Continue to assess the victim(s) and the environment even after you start treatment. As conditions change, you may need to adjust what you do.
❑ bystanders. If there are bystanders and you think they can help you, use them. Bystanders can help a lot during first aid and other emergencies. They can call for medical help, help remove victims from the water, perform first aid, etc. (See page 4-2 for more detailed information on what bystanders can do and how to use them effectively.)
❑ first aid skills. Be realistic about your first aid skills and the skills of those with you, and let this realism guide your first aid efforts. This could help prevent further injury to the victim. If you're not sure what you can do in a first aid emergency, get help.

6.4 Conduct the Primary Assessment

After making sure the rescue environment won't endanger you or the victim, do a *primary assessment* of the victim's condition. In this assessment, you check the ABC priorities (see Chapter 7) and identify any life-threatening condition:
✓ Determine the victim's level of consciousness.
✓ If the victim is conscious, ask simple questions ("What happened?" "What's your name?").
✓ If there's no response, pinch the skin or rub a knuckle on the victim's sternum.

Level of Consciousness
Level of consciousness is an extremely important vital sign. Here are the definitions of different levels:
❑ conscious alert – the victim is oriented to time, place, and person
❑ conscious confused – the victim is awake but has trouble with questions
❑ unconscious, reacts to voice
❑ unconscious, reacts to pain
❑ unconscious, does not react.

✓ If there is still no response, send a second rescuer or bystander to contact EMS and return with an AED if available (see page 3-3).
✓ Maintain an open airway (see pages 7-2 and 7-3).
✓ Assess breathing (see page 7-3).
✓ Look for signs of significant bleeding.

6.5   Get a History of the Victim and the Emergency

Talk to the victim to find out what happened, where he or she is injured, and whether the victim's medical history needs to be considered. You can also get information from a conscious victim or witnesses. Ask questions like these to complete a history:

❑ Where does it hurt? Can you describe the pain? Have you had this before?

❑ How long have you been in pain? Can you describe how it started?

❑ What have you been doing today? What were you doing before this happened?

❑ Are you under a doctor's care? When did you last see your doctor? Why did you last see your doctor?

❑ Are you on any medication? Have you taken any medication today? What kind? How much?

❑ Do you have any allergies?

❑ Have you eaten today? What have you eaten?

If possible, write down the answers to these questions, or have a bystander do it. Give the information to EMS personnel.

Making First Contact with Victims
✓ Start reassuring victims right away — they need comfort and reassurance because of the rescue situation and their injuries.
✓ Say "Hello," and introduce yourself.
✓ Ask if you can help.
✓ Learn and use victims' names.
✓ Assure them of your skills and experience as a lifesaver.

Is There a Spinal Injury?
The possibility of a spinal injury complicates first aid efforts:
✓ Continue to concern yourself with the lifesaving priorities while caring for a spinal injury.
✓ Look for clues at the emergency scene. Was there a fall or a blow to the head? Can anyone tell you about the injury?
✓ If the victim is unconscious, if illness isn't the suspected cause, and if the scene suggests a spinal injury is likely, continue your assessment as if there is a spinal injury.
✓ When you suspect a spinal injury, avoid moving the victim, and maintain airway, breathing, and circulation according to the modifications outlined in pages 5-18 and 5-19.
✓ In the secondary assessment, check carefully for swelling, deformity, discoloration, and sensation.

6.6 Conduct the Secondary Assessment

Once the primary assessment is complete and all life-threatening conditions have been dealt with (including the ABCs and calling EMS), do a *head-to-toe* examination. The purpose of this examination is to determine whether there are other injuries, illnesses, or complicating factors:

✓ Check all areas of the body for pain, swelling, deformity, discoloration, and bleeding.
✓ Check for the specific signs and symptoms identified in the figure on page 6-7.
✓ Check for necklaces, bracelets, cards, etc., identifying a medical condition (Medic Alert bracelets, for instance).
✓ Assess the vital signs to assess changes in condition:
  ● *Assess breathing.* Look, listen, and feel close to the victim's mouth. Note the rate, regularity, and rhythm of breathing. Gurgling, wheezing, or other abnormal sounds and odors provide clues to the victim's condition.

Brachial pulse check

  ● *Assess circulation.* Start CPR immediately if the victim is unresponsive and not breathing or not breathing normally (gasping). Apply an AED as soon as it arrives. If the victim is breathing, check pulse to assess circulation. Check the pulse *rate* (at rest, it is normally 60 to 100 beats per minute for adults, 80 to 100 beats per minute for children, and 100 to 150 beats per minute for newborns), *rhythm* (regular or irregular, with an irregular pulse a sign of potential difficulty), and *quality* (strong in healthy individuals, weak or "thready" among those whose cardiovascular system is failing).

Carotid pulse check

Radial pulse check

  ● Record the victim's pulse rate and rhythm at least once, and send this information to hospital with the victim. If possible, include information on the pulse's quality.
  ● Check the victim's *skin temperature* (normal, warm, or cool).
  ● Check the victim's *skin condition* (normal, dry, or clammy).
  ● Check the victim's *skin color*—normal, pale, red, cherry red, bluish, yellowish, and so on. (Skin color varies with race, general condition, and health. To check for cyanosis (blue-colored lips and skin under the fingernails) in dark-skinned victims, look under the eyelids, lips, or nails to see if the pink color has changed to blue.)

> **Signs and Symptoms**
> An assessment is an evaluation of the victim's signs and symptoms.
> ❑ Signs are the indications of the victim's condition that you can observe in him or her. You will look for signs in your primary and secondary assessments.
> ❑ Symptoms are the indications of the victim's condition that he or she can feel. Through a verbal assessment of the history, the victim can tell you the symptoms he or she is experiencing.

✓ Assess the victim's diagnostic signs:
- *eyes*. Pupils should be equal and round, and they should respond to light. Unequal pupils indicate the possibility of an internal injury to the head. Most people have round pupils. Pupils normally constrict when exposed to more intense light and dilate when light is diminished.
- *ability to move*. Note and investigate any change in the ability to move the entire body or parts of it.
- *reaction to pain*. Reactions to pain are to be expected. The normal response includes a description or an expression of pain, a position that minimizes pain, protection of the injured area, and movement away from the source of pain. The responses of unconscious victims can vary considerably. Try to stimulate unconscious victims with noise (clapping, shouting) and physical stimuli (gently shaking the shoulders, rubbing the sternum). Note and report any response that could be considered abnormal (for instance, leg movement when an arm is stimulated). Do the same for any response that is absent. Both are indications of the severity of the victim's difficulty.

Personal Safety in Assessments

❑ In many rescues, you'll come into contact with fluids from the victim's body—mainly blood, vomit, or spittle.

❑ Disposable gloves should be in every first aid kit (see page 6-8 for information on the contents of these kits). USE them in first aid situations to avoid the risk of cross-contamination from blood, mucus, urine, or other bodily fluids (from bacteria and viruses, for instance).

❑ Dispose of gloves after using them.

❑ The most important prevention against cross-contamination is to wash your hands with warm water and soap (preferably liquid soap) for 1-2 minutes. Then rinse your hands and dry them thoroughly. This should be done as soon as possible after performing a rescue or administering first aid.

Head-to-Toe Examination

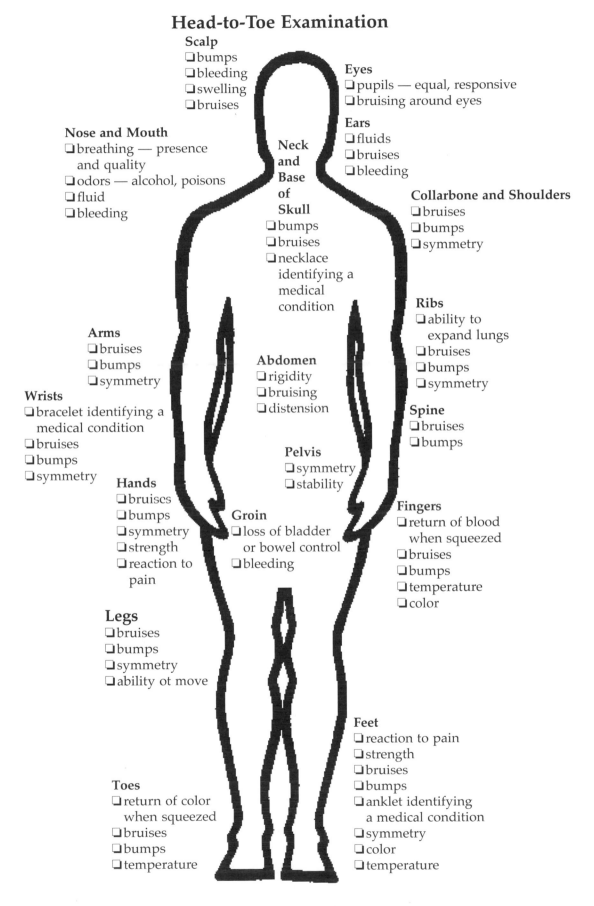

Scalp
- bumps
- bleeding
- swelling
- bruises

Eyes
- pupils — equal, responsive
- bruising around eyes

Ears
- fluids
- bruises
- bleeding

Nose and Mouth
- breathing — presence and quality
- odors — alcohol, poisons
- fluid
- bleeding

Neck and Base of Skull
- bumps
- bruises
- necklace identifying a medical condition

Collarbone and Shoulders
- bruises
- bumps
- symmetry

Arms
- bruises
- bumps
- symmetry

Wrists
- bracelet identifying a medical condition
- bruises
- bumps
- symmetry

Abdomen
- rigidity
- bruising
- distension

Ribs
- ability to expand lungs
- bruises
- bumps
- symmetry

Spine
- bruises
- bumps

Pelvis
- symmetry
- stability

Hands
- bruises
- bumps
- symmetry
- strength
- reaction to pain

Groin
- loss of bladder or bowel control
- bleeding

Fingers
- return of blood when squeezed
- bruises
- bumps
- temperature
- color

Legs
- bruises
- bumps
- symmetry
- ability ot move

Feet
- reaction to pain
- strength
- bruises
- bumps
- anklet identifying a medical condition
- symmetry
- color
- temperature

Toes
- return of color when squeezed
- bruises
- bumps
- temperature

First Aid Kits
First aid kits should be
✓ easily accessible
✓ well organized
✓ water resistant or waterproof

✓ clearly labelled "First Aid"
✓ in a bright-colored container

Recommended Equipment and Supplies
❑ Please check local guidelines and legislation for area-specific equipment required.
❑ Equipment and supplies for first aid kits fall into several categories (see below):
  ● Basic — items that must be immediately available when EMS is readily accessible.
  ● Advanced — items that are necessary if EMS is not necessarily accessible.
  ● Extras — items that are useful to have but are *not* readily. When the first aid kit is a "base" kit for a recreational facility, items from this list should be considered.
❑ Leaders such as lifeguards or instructors should also include the following in their kit:
  ● EMS phone numbers
  ● accident report forms
  ● pencil
  ● matches in waterproof container
  ● flashlight
  ● sunscreen, lip balm

  ● participants' medical information
  ● patient monitoring charts
  ● quarter for coin-operated telephones
  ● pocket knife
  ● whistle

Contents of a First Aid Kit
❑ Basic:
  ● Attendant scissors
  ● Surgical gloves
  ● Antiseptic towelettes
  ● Sterile telfa pads (individually wrapped 25 X 10 cm)
  ● Sterile gauze pads   individually wrapped 10 X 10 cm)
  ● Bandage strips or assorted adhesive dressings

  ● Tweezers
  ● Cotton-tip applicators
  ● Wound closures (e.g., Steristrips)
  ● Absorbent pads (unscented sanitary napkins)
  ● Adhesive tape (2 cm)
  ● Adhesive tape 5(cm)
  ● Cloth triangular bandages, at least 3
  ● Crepe bandages (2)

❑ Advanced:
  ● Parrafin-impregnated gauze dressing e.g., Jelonet individually wrapped)
  ● Metal splints (4)
  ● Spinal board

  ● Cloth triangular bandages, at least 7
  ● Ice, ice pack, or instant cold pack
  ● Sandbags/head rolls
  ● ASA tablets (e.g., Aspirin)

❑ Extras:
  ● Razor and blades
  ● Thermometers (oral and rectal ranging from 32° to 45° Celsius)
  ● Additional rolls adhesive tape (2 cm)
  ● Waterproof, air-permeable dressing (e.g., Jelonet individually wrapped)

  ● Additional cloth triangular bandages
  ● Blood pressure cuff and stethoscope
  ● Large syringe
  ● Pressure dressing ASA tablets (e.g., Aspirin)

❑ Luxuries:
  ● Penlight
  ● Finger splints

  ● Sterile saline solution
  ● Forearm tendonitis splints

6.7   Want to Know More?

Huint, Richard. *A First Aid Guide for Lifeguards*. Montreal: AquaLude Inc., 1987.
> This booklet presents possible signs and symptoms and first aid treatments for a variety of conditions. It is aimed at lifeguards and aquatics instructors.

Lifesaving Society. *Alert: Lifeguarding in Action*. Ottawa: Royal Life Saving Society Canada, 1993.
> *Alert* is the text of the National Lifeguard Service. Designed for professional lifeguards, *Alert* presents information on accident prevention and rescue skills and procedures.

Lifesaving Society. *Canadian First Aid Manual*. Toronto: First edition, April 2005, ninth printing, revised, November 2011.
> The *Canadian First Aid Manual* is the comprehensive reference text for Lifesaving Society first aid training courses.

Chapter 7
Lifesaving Priorities: The ABCs

7.1   Introduction

As a lifesaver, you may be faced with life-threatening emergencies that occur in, on, or near the water. For example, a picnicker at a beach might have a heart attack, or someone might fall on the dock at the cottage and injure himself or herself.

When emergencies involve the ABCs — Airway, Breathing, or Circulation — you must act *fast*. If victims don't receive treatment, their chances of survival drop quickly as time passes.

This chapter describes the procedures to follow when dealing with ABC priorities. It shows how to handle possible complications in airway management and choking, discusses when and how to use rescue breathing, and presents detailed information on cardiopulmonary resuscitation (CPR).

> **Age of victim**
>
> Unless specifically noted, the techniques described in this chapter are for adults.
> Use the following age guidelines when selecting techniques:
> ❑ Adult—8 years and older
> ❑ Child—1 to 8 years
> ❑ Infant—birth to 1 year

7.2   The ABC Priorities

In all rescues, follow the ABC priorities when starting resuscitation attempts on a victim:

❑ **A**irway—maintain an open airway
❑ **B**reathing— perform a quick, visual check (5 sec.) for absent or abnormal breathing
❑ **C**irculation—if the victim is not breathing, or not breathing effectively (gasping), start CPR. If the victim was found on land, start CPR with compressions. If found in the water, start with 2 rescue breaths. Apply an AED as soon as it arrives.

Before You Start Any Rescue . . .

✓ Survey the scene for any *hazards* to yourself and the victim (hazards include electrical wires, fires, broken glass, harmful gas, etc.). Either remove hazards, or move the victim away from the hazards.

✓ *Determine unresponsiveness.* Gently shake the victim and shout "Are you okay"? If the victim doesn't respond, call the Emergency Medical System (EMS) right away. (EMS is a community-wide system for responding to emergencies. It includes police, fire, and ambulance services.) Send a bystander if one is available; otherwise, go yourself.

A: Maintain an Open Airway

Opening and maintaining an airway is perhaps the most important action in a rescue. The tongue and pharynx may obstruct the airway and prevent breathing. Awareness of the airway and the potential for obstruction is an important priority in the management of unconscious persons.

Head-tilt

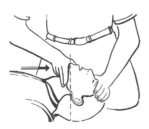

Chin-lift

✓ Open the airway using the head-tilt/chin-lift technique:
  ● *If the victim is an adult,*
    — place one hand on the victim's forehead, and apply firm backward (downward) pressure with the palm to tilt the head back.
    — place the first two fingers of the other hand under the bony part of the lower jaw, near the chin. Lift to bring the chin forward (upward) and almost close the teeth. If you are using a rescue breathing pocket mask, you may find that you can also lift the chin by hooking your fingers under the angle of the jaw and gently lifting the jaw up.
  ● *If the victim is a child or infant,*
    — be careful not to overextend the neck.

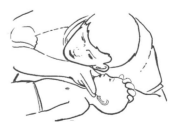

Don't overextend the neck

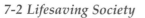

Airway Management in Drowning Victims

Water-related accidents present unique challenges to rescuers. In most documented cases, airway management in drowning victims has been a significant challenge. Rescuers need to be extremely attentive to clearing fluids. The amount of fluid and vomit that needs to be managed is often unexpected. Rescuers may therefore need to place the victim in a recovery or lateral position in order to clear the airway of fluid and other debris. Rescuers must be aware of the potential challenge and remember that airway management is both the priority and the challenge.

Recovery position

B: Assess the Victim's Breathing, and Start CPR If Needed

✓ Determine whether the victim is breathing normally, having trouble breathing, or not breathing at all:
- ● Perform a quick, visual check (5 sec.) for absent or abnormal breathing. Look for chest movement and listen to the victim's breathing.

✓ If a responsive victim is having trouble breathing, find out why.

C: Start CPR if Needed

If an unresponsive victim is not breathing, or not breathing normally (gasping), perform CPR. If the victim was found on land, start CPR with chest compressions. If found in the water, start with rescue breaths. (These techniques are described in Sections 7.4 and 7.5.) Apply an AED as soon as it arrives.

Quick, visual check for breathing

Is There a Spinal Injury?

The possibility of a spinal injury complicates first aid efforts:

✓ Continue to concern yourself with the lifesaving priorities while caring for a spinal injury.

✓ Look for clues at the emergency scene. Was there a fall or a blow to the head? Can anyone tell you about the injury?

✓ If the victim is unconscious, if illness isn't the suspected cause, and if the scene suggests a spinal injury is likely, continue your assessment as if there is a spinal injury.

✓ When you suspect a spinal injury, avoid moving the victim. Maintain airway, breathing, and circulation (see pages 5-18 and 5-19).

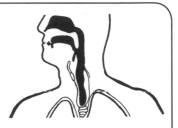

The Anatomy and Physiology of the ABCs
<u>Airway</u>

Airway refers to the parts of the respiratory system that connect the lungs to the "outside world." These parts include the nose, mouth, pharynx (throat), larynx (voice box, or Adam's apple), and trachea (windpipe).

<u>Breathing</u>

Breathing is the exchange of air between the lungs and the atmosphere. The air passages consist of the nose, mouth, pharynx, larynx, trachea, bronchi, and bronchioles. These passages lead to the true lung tissues, or alveoli, the clusters of air spaces at the end of the bronchioles. In the alveoli, oxygen and carbon dioxide pass between the atmosphere and the blood. Because of the microscopic distances involved, this exchange is almost instantaneous.

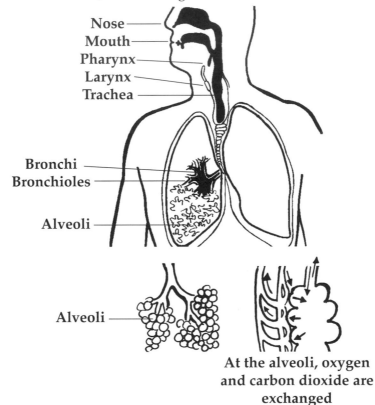

At the alveoli, oxygen and carbon dioxide are exchanged

The air-containing lungs are elastic. When you breathe in, your lungs inflate—the diaphragm moves down, the lower ribs swing outward to increase the width of the chest, and the upper ribs and breastbone move outward to increase the front-to-back diameter. Breathing out happens passively, as the muscles relax.

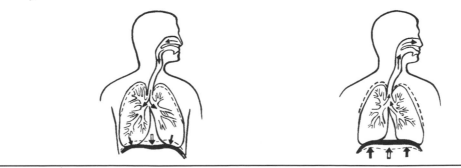

The Anatomy and Physiology of the ABCs (cont'd)

Breathing is largely automatically controlled by the "respiratory control centre," deep within the brain. When the muscle cells are actively working—for example, during swimming—the cells produce carbon dioxide, which is picked up by the blood. The rise in blood carbon dioxide is sensed by the respiratory control centre, which causes an increase in breathing.

About 21% of room air consists of oxygen. About 16% of *exhaled* air consists of oxygen. This difference shows that there is plenty of oxygen in exhaled air for use in rescue breathing to rescue a non-breathing victim.

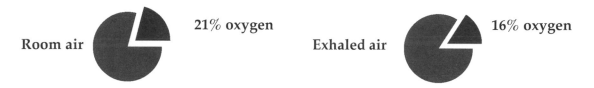

Room air   **21% oxygen**   Exhaled air   **16% oxygen**

Circulation

The circulatory system is a closed "plumbing" system of heart, arteries, capillaries, and veins through which blood flows continuously. Its purpose is to transport oxygen and other materials to the cells of the body and to remove wastes, including carbon dioxide.

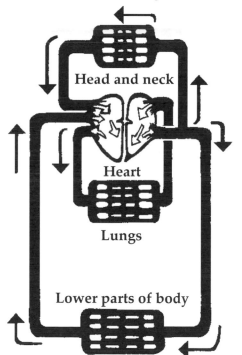

Head and neck

Heart

Lungs

Lower parts of body

- ❏ The circulatory system conducts blood through a simple circuit powered by two pumps working simultaneously. The pumps are the right and left ventricles of the heart.
- ❏ Darker venous blood, having given up some of its oxygen to the cells, flows centrally through veins back to the heart, where it is pumped to the lungs for oxygenation. The blood returns from the lungs to the heart and is pumped throughout the body through the aorta and arteries.
- ❏ The blood flow then divides into many pulmonary capillaries, where blood is re-oxygenated after it releases its carbon dioxide.
- ❏ The aorta and larger arteries stretch with each ventricular beat. When the circulatory system is functioning properly, all tissues in the body receive a full supply of blood—and with it oxygen.

7.3   Coping with Complications during the ABCs

Complications can occur during ABC emergencies. This section describes how to deal with airway obstruction complications.

Airway Obstruction

Airway obstruction (choking) can occur in conscious or unconscious victims. If the conscious victim does not receive prompt treatment, he or she will quickly become unconscious. Airway obstruction is most often caused by food or other objects getting stuck in the throat.

You need to know how to treat the following kinds of airway obstructions:
- ❑ mild airway obstruction
- ❑ severe airway obstruction in conscious victims
- ❑ severe airway obstruction in conscious victims who become unconscious
- ❑ severe airway obstruction in unconscious victims
- ❑ vomiting.

Mild Airway Obstruction
With a mild obstruction, the victim has adequate air exchange. The victim can speak or cry, breathe and cough effectively. Encourage the victim to cough. Do not interfere while the victim is clearing the airway blockage by coughing.

Severe Airway Obstruction
In a severe obstruction, the airway is blocked. The victim nods "yes" when asked "Are you choking?", clutches neck or cannot speak, cry or make any sound. The rescuer must take action to clear the obstruction.

Severe Airway Obstruction in Conscious Victims
Adults and Children. The procedure is as follows:
✓ Ask "Are you choking?"
✓ If you don't hear any sounds (speaking, coughing, or other noises), assume complete airway obstruction.
✓ Clear the airway using one or more of the techniques described in the following pages.
✓ If the selected technique does not work (e.g., after 5 abdominal thrusts), attempt another technique (e.g., 5 back blows). Continue alternating techniques until the object is cleared (the victim can breathe) or the victim becomes unconscious.

> **Obstructed Airway Techniques**
> Back blows, abdominal thrusts or chest thrusts are effective for relieving severe airway obstruction in conscious adults and children. These techniques should be applied in rapid sequence until the obstruction is relieved or the victim becomes unconscious. More than one technique may be needed; there is insufficient evidence to determine which should be used first.
> Some jurisdictions follow a standardized protocol. E.g., for Emergency or Standard First Aid in Quebec, abdominal thrusts or chest compressions are used; while in Ontario, 5 back blows alternate with 5 abdominal thrusts. Follow provincial protocols.

Infants. The procedure is as follows:
- ✓ If you don't hear any sounds (gurgling, coughing, or other noises), assume complete airway obstruction.
- ✓ Give 5 back blows followed by 5 chest thrusts, and repeat until they are effective (the object is cleared and the victim is breathing) or the victim becomes unconscious.

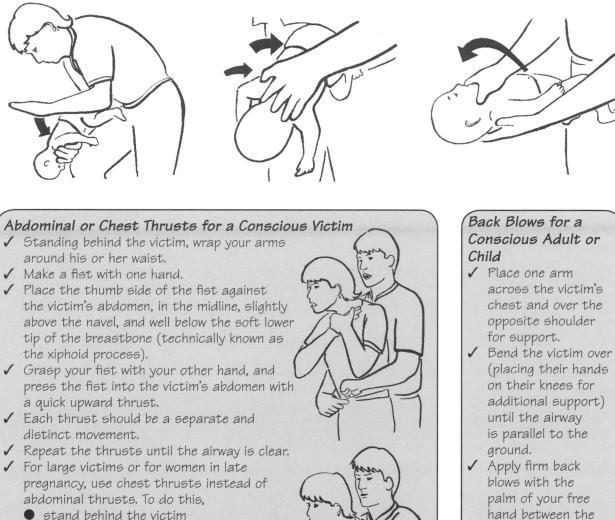

Abdominal or Chest Thrusts for a Conscious Victim
- ✓ Standing behind the victim, wrap your arms around his or her waist.
- ✓ Make a fist with one hand.
- ✓ Place the thumb side of the fist against the victim's abdomen, in the midline, slightly above the navel, and well below the soft lower tip of the breastbone (technically known as the xiphoid process).
- ✓ Grasp your fist with your other hand, and press the fist into the victim's abdomen with a quick upward thrust.
- ✓ Each thrust should be a separate and distinct movement.
- ✓ Repeat the thrusts until the airway is clear.
- ✓ For large victims or for women in late pregnancy, use chest thrusts instead of abdominal thrusts. To do this,
  - ● stand behind the victim
  - ● circle his or her chest under the armpits
  - ● grab your fist with the other hand, and place the thumb side in the centre of the victim's sternum
  - ● press with quick backward thrusts.

Note: Abdominal thrusts can be performed effectively while standing in shallow water.

Back Blows for a Conscious Adult or Child
- ✓ Place one arm across the victim's chest and over the opposite shoulder for support.
- ✓ Bend the victim over (placing their hands on their knees for additional support) until the airway is parallel to the ground.
- ✓ Apply firm back blows with the palm of your free hand between the shoulder blades.

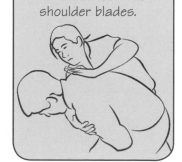

Severe Airway Obstruction in Conscious Victims
Who Become Unconscious

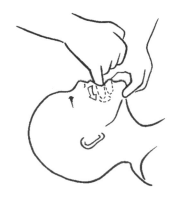

Adults and Children. The procedure is as follows:
1 Assist the victim to the floor to prevent injury. If victims are in the water, remove them, and place them on a firm surface—it increases the chances that chest compressions will be effective.
2 If the victim does not respond, send a bystander to call EMS and return with an AED if one is available. If you are alone with an adult victim, call EMS without delay and return with an AED if one is immediately available. If you are alone with a child, perform 2 minutes of resuscitation and then call EMS and return with an AED if available.
3 Perform 30 chest compressions. Open the mouth and look inside for the obstruction. If you see it, remove it.
4 Open the airway, and try to blow air in (ventilate). If the airway is still obstructed, reposition the victim's head, and try again to ventilate.
5 If the airway is still obstructed, perform 30 chest compressions. Use same landmarking and compression technique as used for adult or child CPR (see pages 7-13 and 7-14).
6 Repeat steps 3 to 5 until they are effective (the object is cleared and the victim is breathing). Continue until EMS arrives.
7 If the victim is breathing or starts breathing, treat for shock (including placing him or her in the recovery position).

Infants. The procedure is as follows:
1 Place the infant on a firm surface.
2 If the victim doesn't respond, send a bystander to phone EMS. If you are alone with an infant, perform 2 minutes of resuscitation and then call EMS. See AED Use on Infants, page 7-15.
3 Perform 30 chest compressions. Open the mouth and look inside for the obstruction. If you see it, remove it.
4 Open the airway, and try to blow air in (ventilate). If the airway is still obstructed, reposition the victim's head, and try again to ventilate.
5 If the airway is still obstructed, perform 30 chest compressions. Use same landmarking and compression technique as used for infant CPR (see pages 7-14 and 7-15).
6 Repeat steps 3 to 5 until they are effective (the object is cleared and the victim is breathing). Continue until EMS arrives.

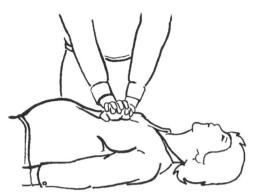

Severe Airway Obstruction in Unconscious Victims

1 Survey the scene for any hazards.
2 If the victim does not respond, send a bystander to call EMS and return with an AED if one is available. If you are alone with an adult victim, call EMS without delay and return with an AED if one is immediately available. If you are alone with child or infant victims, perform 2 minutes of resuscitation and then call EMS and return with an AED if available.
3 Open the airway using the head-tilt/chin-lift technique. Perform a quick, visual check for absent or abnormal breathing. Look for chest movement and listen to the victim's breathing.
4 If an unresponsive victim is not breathing, or not breathing normally (gasping), perform 30 compressions if there no history of submersion. Use the CPR landmarking and compression technique appropriate for the victim type (see pages 7-13 to 7-15).
5 Attempt to give 2 normal (not deep) rescue breaths, each delivered over 1 second and making the chest rise (allow for exhalation between breaths). If air does not go in on the first breath, reposition the airway and try again. If the airway is still obstructed, perform 30 chest compressions.
6 Open the mouth and look inside for the obstruction. If you see it, remove it.
7 Repeat steps 4 to 6 until they are effective (the object is cleared and the victim is breathing). Continue until EMS arrives.
8 If the victim is breathing or starts breathing, treat for shock (including placing him or her in the recovery position).

Vomiting

Most victims vomit during or after a rescue. Vomit is full of acids, and if they go down the windpipe (trachea) and into the lungs, it will be hard—if not impossible—to resuscitate the victim. It is therefore very important to prevent vomit or any other fluid from going into the lungs.

✓ Be prepared to react to vomiting very quickly.
✓ Turn the victim immediately to a position that allows fluid to drain.

> The upper airway can be obstructed by foreign matter such as plant debris from water, dentures, gum, food, broken teeth, blood, or mucus. Turn the victim to his or her side, and remove this material from the mouth and throat with sweeps of the finger.

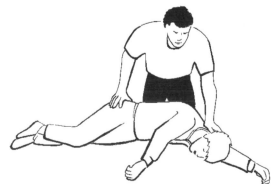

7.4   Rescue Breathing

Rescue breathing refers to various techniques in which expired air passes directly from a rescuer to a victim not breathing on his or her own. Rescue breaths are performed as part of the CPR sequence on victims who are not breathing or not breathing normally. Stand-alone rescue breathing may be performed prior to initiating CPR if a victim is far from the shore or removal is delayed (the rescuer is waiting for bystanders to help remove the victim from the water).

Rescue breathing in the water should only be attempted if the rescuer can effectively maintain the victim's airway above the water and deal with complications such as vomiting. See Appendix B for Lifesaving Society policy guidelines on rescue breathing practice.

Rescue breathing has the following features:

> The body's supply of oxygen is usually sufficient to sustain life for about 4 minutes. This is why you must quickly transport victims to where rescue breathing can be started.

✓ It can be started early in a rescue because no special equipment is needed.
✓ It's versatile. Rescuers can use it almost anywhere they find a victim (including the water).
✓ The rescuer can tell right away if air is going into the lungs.
✓ Success in rescue breathing does NOT depend on the rescuer's size.
✓ The rescuer is close to the victim's face. This means the rescuer can quickly see and respond to signs of recovery or complications.

Rescue Breathing Technique

1 Survey the scene for hazards, and make the area safe.
2 Establish unresponsiveness. Gently shake and shout, and ask "Are you okay"? If the victim does not respond, send a bystander to call EMS and return with an AED if one is available. If you are alone with an adult victim, call EMS without delay and return with an AED if one is immediately available. If you are alone with child or infant victims, perform 2 minutes of resuscitation and then call EMS and return with an AED if available. See *AED Use on Infants*, page 7-14.
3 Open the airway using the head-tilt/chin-lift technique. Perform a quick, visual check for absent or abnormal breathing. Look for chest movement and listen to the victim's breathing.
4 If an unresponsive victim is not breathing, or not breathing normally (gasping), start CPR with compressions. If there is a history of submersion, start CPR with 2 rescue breaths. If the rescuer is unable to start CPR (e.g., distance to shore or delayed removal from the water), stand-alone rescue breathing should be initiated (2 initial breaths followed up by 1 breath every 5 seconds for an adult and 1 breath every 3 seconds for a child or infant).
5 Rescue breathing – give 2 initial rescue breaths (normal breaths, not deep), each delivered over 1 second and each making the chest rise. Watch the chest rise and allow exhalation between the breaths.

● Pinch the nose, and seal the victim's mouth with your mouth. With small children and infants, you might have to seal the mouth and nose with your mouth because their faces are small. Also, extend their neck gently.

Rescue Breathing in Water

General Recommendations
✓ Ensure your own safety and that of the victim.
✓ Call EMS.
✓ Start rescue breathing as soon as you and the victim are in a stable position.
✓ When you are doing rescue breathing in the water, only the head-tilt manoeuvre may be possible.
✓ Keep the victim's nose pinched throughout rescue breathing in the water.
✓ Get out of cold water as soon as possible if you started rescue breathing in water.
✓ Strong currents make it harder to control the victim. So move away from them, or work *with* currents, not against them.

Rescue Breathing in Shallow Water
✓ Find a secure location where
● slips and submersion will not occur
● complications can be treated if they occur
● other rescuers can come to help
● removal is possible.

Rescue Breathing in Deep Water
❏ Deep-water rescue breathing is an advanced lifesaving skill (see page 5-23). It can be very tiring, and you risk injury when you do it.
❏ Consider deep-water rescue breathing only if you have a reaching assist and can stabilize yourself and the victim.
❏ Deep-water rescue breathing should generally be avoided because it is hard to maintain an airway and nearly impossible to perform if the victim vomits.

Special Rescue Breathing Techniques
There will be times when mouth-to-mouth rescue breathing may not be possible because of injury to the victim's mouth or previous surgery. In such cases, you will have to use one of the following rescue breathing techniques:
❏ mouth-to-nose rescue breathing. When it isn't possible to seal the victim's mouth, try mouth-to-nose rescue breathing. Close the victim's mouth, and seal your mouth around the victim's nose. Give 2 normal breaths, and observe the chest rise to see that air goes in.

Rescue breathing rate
Rescue breathing alone is performed at a rate of 1 breath every 5 seconds for adults; 1 breath every 3 seconds for children and infants.

Rescue breathing in shallow water

Mouth-to-nose rescue breathing

❏ mouth-to-stoma rescue breathing. Some people have had surgery to remove part of their trachea (windpipe). They breathe through a hole called a stoma in the front of the neck. Perform rescue breathing using the stoma. Observe the chest rise to see that air goes in.

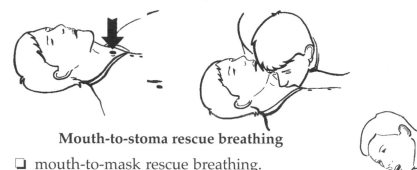

Mouth-to-stoma rescue breathing

Handkerchiefs and tissues are not effective barriers and do not decrease the risk of cross-contamination from bodily fluids (from bacteria and viruses, for instance).

❏ mouth-to-mask rescue breathing. Mouthpieces, face masks, and face shields are barriers that offer protection against disease in rescue breathing. Those who are expected to routinely provide first aid are advised to keep such a barrier handy in a first aid kit. Follow the manufacturer's instructions to learn how to use barriers properly.

Face mask barrier

7.5   CPR and AED

Cardiopulmonary resuscitation (CPR) is a sequence of chest compressions and ventilations designed to maintain a victim's circulation. CPR can be performed by one or two rescuers.

Technique for two-rescuer CPR is the same as that for one-rescuer CPR, except that one rescuer performs compressions while the second provides ventilations. It is easier to co-ordinate two-rescuer CPR if the rescuer performing compressions counts out loud. Alternatively, two CPR-trained rescuers can take turns performing one-rescuer CPR. When the AED arrives on scene, one rescuer performs CPR while the second rescuer begins the AED protocol. Rescuers should alternate CPR and AED every two minutes to minimize fatigue.

The chart on page 7-17 presents the steps in one-rescuer and two-rescuer CPR and AED use.

Automated External Defibrillator (AED)

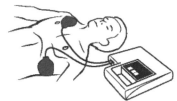

The upper-right chest pad should not go over top of the sternum, clavicle or nipple. The lower-left pad should wrap around the rib cage. Do not place on the abdomen.

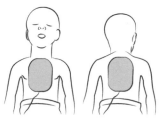

If a child victim is small, do not let the pads touch each other. If necessary, place one pad on the centre of the chest and the other on the back between the shoulder blades.

Adult and Child: One-Rescuer CPR and AED

1 Survey the scene for hazards.
2 Determine unresponsiveness. Gently shake the victim, and shout "Are you okay"? If the victim does not respond, send a bystander to call EMS and return with an AED if one is available. If you are alone with an adult victim, call EMS without delay and return with an AED if immediately available. If you are alone with a child, perform 2 minutes of resuscitation and then call EMS and return with an AED (if available).
3 Open the airway using the head-tilt/chin-lift technique. Perform a quick, visual check for absent or abnormal breathing. Look for chest movement and listen to the victim's breathing.
4 If an unresponsive victim is not breathing, or not breathing normally (gasping), start CPR with 30 compressions. If there is a history of submersion, start CPR with 2 rescue breaths.
   - Landmark on the centre of the chest between the nipples and position both hands on the sternum, one hand on top of the other for vertical compressions.
   - Keep elbows locked and straight during compressions.
   - Perform compressions at a rate of at least 100 per minute and allow for full chest recoil between compressions.
   - Adult – Compress at least 5 cm (2 in.).
   - Child – Compress at least 1/3 the front-back diameter of the chest up to 5 cm (2 in.).
5 Rescue breathing – give 2 normal (not deep) breaths, each breath delivered over 1 second and each making the chest rise. Watch the chest rise and allow exhalation between the breaths.
6 Continue cycles of 30 compressions and 2 ventilations until EMS takes over treatment, the AED arrives or the victim begins to move. If the victim begins to move, reassess ABCs and treat appropriately.
7 When the AED arrives, turn on the power and follow the prompts.
8 Expose the chest and if necessary, shave and dry the skin prior to the application of the AED pads. Apply the pads properly as required for adults and children.
9 Do not touch the victim while the AED is analyzing for a heart rhythm or during a SHOCK sequence. After a "shock" or "no-shock" prompt, perform 2 minutes of CPR unless the victim shows signs of life.

Adult/child landmarking and adult/child CPR

> **Automated External Defibrillator (AED)**
> An AED is a sophisticated computerized device designed to restore the normal rhythm of the heart with an electric shock. AEDs and AED-trained responders are located in many public facilities such as community recreation centres, shopping malls, seniors' centres and airports.
> Access to early defibrillation is a key link in the "Canadian Chain of Survival" and when combined with early and effective CPR can dramatically improve the victim's chance of survival. For more information about AED training, contact the Lifesaving Society.

> **Child Compressions**
> For child compressions, the rescuer can perform compressions using 1 or 2 hands as long as suitable compression is achieved.

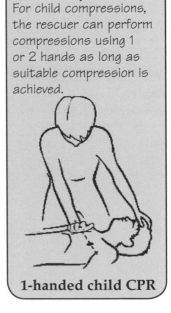

1-handed child CPR

Compression Rate
Compression rate refers to the speed of compressions, not the actual number of compressions delivered in one minute. A compression rate of about 100 per minute will result in delivery of fewer than 100 chest compressions per minute by a rescuer who must interupt compressions to deliver rescue breaths.

AED Use on Infants
The need for defibrillation on infants is uncommon, and the preferred treatment involves the use of a manual defibrillator by trained health care professionals. In an emergency, an AED could be used on an infant. If so, use pediatric pads if available. Otherwise, use adult pads.

CPR with Pregnant Victims
Put a pillow or some wedge-shaped object under the right side of the woman's abdomen — it shifts the uterus to the left side. This helps blood return to the heart.

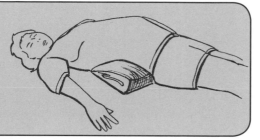

Infant: One-Rescuer CPR

1 Survey the scene for hazards.
2 Determine unresponsiveness. Gently shake the victim, and shout "Are you okay"? If the victim does not respond, send a bystander to call EMS. If you are alone, perform 2 minutes of resuscitation and then call EMS. See *AED Use on Infants*, page 7-14.
3 Open the airway using the head-tilt/chin-lift technique. Perform a quick, visual check for absent or abnormal breathing. Look for chest movement and listen to the victim's breathing.
4 If an unresponsive victim is not breathing or not breathing normally (gasping), start CPR with 30 compressions. If there a history of submersion, start CPR with 2 rescue breaths.
   ● Landmark 1 finger width below the centre of the nipple line and use 2 fingers for compressions.
   ● Perform compressions at a rate of at least 100 per minute and allow for full chest recoil between compressions.
   ● Compress at a depth of at least 1/3 the front-back diameter of the chest up to 4 cm (1.5 in.).
5 Rescue breathing – give 2 gentle puffs sealing over the mouth and nose, each puff delivered over 1 second and each making the chest rise. Watch the chest rise and allow exhalation between breaths.
6 Continue cycles of 30 compressions and 2 ventilations until EMS takes over treatment or the victim begins to move. If the victim begins to move, reassess ABCs and treat appropriately.

Landmarking for infant CPR

Two-Rescuer CPR

Fatigue can begin to affect the effectiveness of compressions in as little as 2 minutes. Two-rescuer CPR allows rescuers to take turns doing compressions and minimize fatigue by changing the person doing compressions about every 5 cycles of 30:2 (about 2 minutes). One-rescuer CPR is done until a second rescuer is available. If EMS and the AED have not been called for, the second rescuer makes the call and returns with an AED if available.

✓ Rescuer 1
  - performs one-rescuer CPR.
✓ Rescuer 2
  - identifies self as trained in CPR
  - calls EMS and returns with an AED (if available) if it hasn't already been done.
✓ One rescuer does chest compressions while other remains at the victim's head, maintains an open airway and gives 2 rescue breaths between each set of 30 compressions. Change the person doing compressions about every 5 cycles of 30:2 (about 2 minutes) to reduce fatigue for the rescuers.
✓ Rescuers should minimize the time it takes to switch positions – less than 10 seconds.
✓ Rescuers communicate and cooperate in decision making and CPR performance.

> **Two Rescuers – Two Choices**
> A second rescuer can replace the first rescuer who becomes fatigued performing one-rescuer CPR. Alternatively, one rescuer performs chest compressions while the other performs rescue breathing, switching roles when the person doing chest compressions tires.

> **Three tips for good, effective CPR:**
> ✓ **Push hard and fast** (rate of 100/min.). Forceful, fast CPR provides better circulation of blood and oxygen.
> ✓ **Allow chest to recoil fully between compressions:** 50% compression, 50% relaxation. Relaxing the pressure on the chest between compressions allows the heart to refill and pump more blood with each compression.
> ✓ **Minimize interruptions in compressions.** Blood flow stops if compressions stop.

Disease Control during Resuscitation Training

Manikins that are used in resuscitation training (including CPR) must be cleaned thoroughly and disinfected after training. Wear gloves when cleaning manikins.

All the parts that come into contact with air must first be cleaned with brushes in soapy water (dishwashing liquid is recommended). The parts are then left to soak for 10 minutes in a disinfecting solution made up of 60 millilitres of household bleach such as Javex to 4 litres of tap water.

The lungs blown into must be disposable and must be discarded promptly after use.

When practising resuscitation skills and CPR using manikins,
- ❑ do not chew gum or eat
- ❑ do not participate in ventilation if you have a respiratory infection (cold, flu, etc.) or open sores on your hands or mouth
- ❑ do not wear lipstick
- ❑ wash your hands before and after working on manikins.

When sharing a manikin during training,
- ✓ dry the face of the manikin with a gauze pad or clean paper towel
- ✓ wipe the face of the manikin with a disinfecting solution (alcohol or bleach; see above), and scrub even inside the manikin's mouth
- ✓ leave the manikin's face wet for 30 seconds before another person takes over the manikin.

One- and Two-Rescuer CPR Summary

1   Check for danger. Establish unresponsiveness (shake/squeeze shoulders, speak into both ears, and ask "Are you okay"?).

2   Phone EMS and retrieve an AED – send a bystander to call EMS and return with an AED if one is available.

   If you are alone with an adult victim, call EMS without delay and return with an AED if one is immediately available.

   If you are alone with a child or infant, call EMS and return with an AED (if one is immediately available) after attempting 2 minutes of resuscitation.

   See *AED Use on Infants*, page 7-14.

3   Check for breathing:

   Position the victim. Turn victim over if necessary to open the airway.

   Open airway. Head-tilt/chin-lift.

   Perform a quick, visual check (5 sec.) for absent or abnormal breathing. Look for chest movement and listen to the victim's breathing.

4   If an unresponsive victim is not breathing, or not breathing normally (gasping), start CPR with 30 compressions. If there is a history of submersion, start CPR with 2 rescue breaths. Adult and Child - Landmark on the center of a line drawn between the nipples and position both hands, one on top of the other for vertical compressions. Keep elbows locked straight during compressions. Infant – Landmark 1 finger width below the centre of the nipple line and use 2 fingers for compressions.

   Depth of compressions: Adult – at least 5 cm (2 in.); Child – at least 1/3 the front-back diameter of the chest up to 5 cm (2 in.); Infant – at least 1/3 the front-back diameter of the chest up to 4 cm (1½ in.).

5   Rescue Breathing: 2 normal (not deep) breaths, each breath delivered over 1 second and each making the chest rise. Watch chest rise and allow exhalation between breaths. Adult and Child - seal mouth, pinch nose, normal breaths. Infant - seal over baby's mouth and nose, blow gentle puffs. If available, use a rescue breathing barrier device.

6.   Continue cycles of 30 compressions and 2 ventilations until EMS takes over treatment, the AED arrives on the scene, or the victim begins to move. If the victim begins to move, reassess ABCs and treat appropriately.

7   Two-rescuer CPR options may include:

   • 2 rescuers take turns doing one-rescuer CPR.

   • 1 rescuer does chest compressions while other does rescue breathing; switch roles about every 5 cycles of 30:2 (about 2 minutes).

8   When the AED arrives on the scene, turn on the power and follow the prompts.

9   Expose the chest and if necessary, shave and dry the skin prior to applying AED pads properly as required for adults and children.

10   Avoid touching the victim while the AED is analyzing for a heart rhythm or during a shock sequence. After a "shock" or "no-shock" prompt, perform 2 minutes of CPR unless the victim shows signs of life.

7.6   Want to Know More?

American Heart Association, *Circulation*, Volume 122, Issue 18_suppl_3; November 2, 2010. Presents 2010 American Heart Association Guidelines for Cardiopulmonary Resuscitation and Emergency Cardiovascular Care Science. Visit: www.circ.ahajournals.org.

Christensen, Anna, editor. *Wilderness First Aid*. Vancouver: Wilderness First Aid and Safety Association, 1986.
> This comprehensive manual is a wealth of information. It covers a variety of injuries in considerable detail and also explores related topics such as legal issues.

La fédération française d'études et de sports sous-marins. *Plongée, santé, sécurité*, third edition. Éditions Ouest-France, n.d.
> This text presents a detailed examination of medical conditions that may result while scuba diving. It also describes the circumstances that contribute to them. The text stresses the safety practices that divers should follow.

Huint, Richard. *Understanding Drowning (and Related Topics)*. Montreal: AquaLude Inc., 1992.
> This text presents detailed information on the physiology of drowning and summarizes significant scientific research on the subject. It is of particular interest to lifeguards and aquatics instructors.

 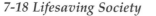

Lifesaving Society. *Alert: Lifeguarding in Action*. Ottawa: Royal Life Saving Society Canada, 1993.
>   *Alert* is the text of the National Lifeguard Service. Designed for professional lifeguards, *Alert* presents information on accident prevention and rescue skills and procedures.

Lifesaving Society. *Canadian First Aid Manual*. Toronto: First edition, April 2005, ninth printing, revised, November 2011.
>   The *Canadian First Aid Manual* is the comprehensive reference text for Lifesaving Society first aid training courses.

Professional Association of Diving Instructors (PADI). *Open Water Dive Manual*. Santa Ana: PADI, 1988.
>   This manual is about the fun and adventure of learning to scuba dive. A manual for candidates in PADI courses, *Open Water Dive Manual* presents information on scuba equipment, clothing, scuba safety, and the physiology and psychology of scuba diving. Information on how to use the decompression tables is also included.

Wilkinson, James, Cameron Bangs, and John Hayward. *Hypothermia, Frostbite and Other Cold Injuries*. Seattle: The Mountaineers, 1986.
>   This is a short but comprehensive work on cold-related injuries and the complications associated with them. It contains an excellent chapter on immersion hypothermia.

Chapter 8
First Aid: The Treatment of Illness or Injury

8.1   Introduction

First aid is the immediate and temporary care of illness or injury. The goals of first aid are—in order—to preserve life, prevent further injury, and promote recovery.

This chapter describes first aid for specific conditions rescuers may encounter. Conditions have been divided into 10 groups on the basis of similarity in causes, signs, or symptoms:

- ❏ shock
- ❏ airway and breathing problems—includes airway obstructions, anaphylaxis, aspiration, asthma, hyperventilation, and respiratory distress
- ❏ circulatory disorders—includes angina, heart attack, cardiac arrest, and stroke
- ❏ bleeding—includes external bleeding, internal abdominal bleeding, and nosebleeds
- ❏ trauma injuries—includes head injuries, spinal injuries, chest wounds, injuries from embedded objects, bites, and eye injuries
- ❏ burns—includes first-degree, second-degree, and third-degree burns
- ❏ medical disorders—includes insulin shock, diabetic coma, tonic-clonic seizures, near-drowning, water intoxication, fainting, and poisoning
- ❏ heat/cold disorders—includes heat cramps, heat exhaustion, heatstroke, frostbite, and hypothermia
- ❏ bone, joint, and soft-tissue disorders—includes bruising, sprains and strains, simple and compound fractures, dislocations, and muscle cramps
- ❏ scuba-diving and skin-diving disorders—includes squeezes, air embolism, and decompression sickness.

This chapter describes each condition, lists prominent signs and symptoms, and summarizes effective treatment. *All* prominent signs and symptoms are listed, but the number observed in an actual *rescue* will vary with the seriousness and extent of the victim's injuries. Suggestions for treatment are presented *in the order treatment should occur.*

> ### Helping with Medication
> Victims suffering from a variety of conditions may have medication they know will help them. You can help victims by:
> - ❏ Getting medication for them.
> - ❏ Helping them take the medication by opening the container it's in or supporting victims while they take medication.
> - ❏ Administering an epinephrine auto-injector according to the package instructions to victims suffering from a life-threatening allergy who cannot do it themselves. Use only the victim's auto-injector, never another person's.
>
> With the exception of an auto-injector, if victims can't administer the medication themselves, DO NOT do it for them.

8.2   Shock

Shock is a depression of the body's circulatory system. Shock occurs when the body is responding to a stress such as physical illness or injury or to emotional or psychological distress. *Expect shock in anyone requiring rescue or first aid.*

Shock can be mild, with few signs and symptoms, or very serious, with life-threatening signs and symptoms. The extent of shock is usually related to the severity of the stress on the body.

> It is your responsibility as a rescuer to assess risk in an emergency. If you are in doubt, call the Emergency Medical System (EMS), and get directions from them. But remember—not all emergencies require EMS.

Signs and Symptoms
✓ Pale, cool, clammy skin
✓ Restlessness, weakness
✓ Fear, anxiety
✓ Confusion, disorientation
✓ Weak, rapid pulse
✓ Shallow, rapid respiration
✓ Blue-colored lips and fingernails (cyanosis)

Treatment
The way to remember treatment for shock is the word WARTS:

1 *Warmth.* Maintain body temperature. If the victim is in the sun, provide shade. If the victim's body is cool, maintain heat.
2 *ABCs:*
   ● Airway—Maintain an open airway
   ● Breathing—assess the victim's breathing and start CPR if needed
   ● Circulation—Monitor responsiveness and breathing. Start CPR if needed.
3 *Rest and assurance.* Reassure the victim, and make sure he or she rests. Pursed-lip breathing (see page 8-4) is a technique you can use to calm the victim. Talk calmly, positively, and personally to the victim. Make eye contact when you talk to him or her, and use a gentle, confident touch. Maintain *your* calm—your ability to cope with stress directly affects the victim, and *that's* your priority.
4 *Treatment.* Treat the *cause* of the stress—the cut, for example, or the heart attack.

5 *Semi-prone (recovery) position.* This is the position of choice for victims. But if the illness or injury indicates that another position would be better, the victim should get into that position. For example, a semi-sitting position is recommended with heart attacks, and spinal victims should be on their back with their head immobilized.

8.3   Airway and Breathing Problems

Airway Obstruction

Airway obstruction (choking) can occur in conscious or unconscious victims. If the conscious victim doesn't receive prompt treatment, he or she will quickly become unconscious. In conscious victims, airway obstruction is most often caused by food or other objects getting stuck in the throat.

Unconscious people lose control of their tongue, and it slips back, blocking the airway and preventing breathing. This is the most common cause of airway obstruction in unconscious people.

See Section 7.3 for detailed information on how to treat airway obstruction.

Anaphylaxis

Anaphylaxis is a severe, often life-threatening allergic reaction. Substances associated with this condition include medications such as penicillin, some foods such as nuts and seafood, bee stings, and some environmental substances such as moulds.

The reaction can be sudden and rapid. People who know they have this condition may wear a necklace, bracelet, etc., identifying a medical condition and may even carry an antidote kit.

Signs and Symptoms
✓ Generalized itchiness, rash (red), hives
✓ Difficulty breathing, including wheezing
✓ Lower level of consciousness (confusion, disorientation)
✓ Swelling of central facial features (lips, tongue, face)

Treatment
1   Some individuals may have medication for this situation – preloaded syringes and tablets to reduce allergic reactions. Help victims administer their medication if they have it.
2   Assess responsiveness, maintain an open airway and assess the victim's breathing. Start CPR if needed.
3   Contact EMS.
4   Treat for shock.
5   Give oxygen if you are trained to do so and it is both medically necessary and available.

The Administration of Oxygen

Basic Principles

❑ Give oxygen if you are trained to do so and it is both medically necessary and available.
❑ Most victims who need oxygen are breathing, perhaps with difficulty.
❑ Victims are best treated with a free-flow inhalator.
❑ Victims with absent or abnormal breathing require CPR.

Procedure

1   Explain to the victim what you'll be doing.
2   Turn on the flow of oxygen using the key and then turn the regulator to 10-15 litres/minute.
3   Approach the victim's face slowly with the mask.
4   Allow the victim to feel the oxygen as it flows.
5   Have the victim breathe from the mask.
6   If the victim is not breathing, or not breathing normally, start CPR. The oxygen mask tubing can be connected to the oxygen port on the pocket mask. Oxygen will be delivered each time the rescuer ventilates the victim.

Precautions

❑ Verify the volume of oxygen contained in the cylinder.
❑ If the cylinder is under high pressure: protect the tank and the valve.
❑ Get rid of all impurities that may be on any equipment, especially products like grease.
❑ Be sure to check the cylinder, its attachments and especially its calibration at least once a year.
❑ Store in a cool place.

The drowning process may result in Acute Respiratory Distress some hours after the initial drowning event and rescue. After rescue from the water, the victim should be sent to hospital if he or she:
• suffered any loss of consciousness
• required resuscitation (rescue breathing, CPR)
• has any concurrent condition (e.g. seizure, spinal injury, asthma)
• has on-going coughing

Pursed-Lip Breathing Asthmatics have trouble getting air out. Pursed-lip breathing occurs when the lips are in a "pucker" position and the victim actively blows the air out in a slow, steady stream. You and the victim can do this together. Inhale through the nose, exhale through the pursed lips, and focus on getting air out.

Aspiration
Aspiration occurs when water or other liquids enter the airway.

Signs and Symptoms
✓ Coughing
✓ Raspy breathing
✓ Pain in the chest
✓ Nausea
✓ Distress, anxiety

Treatment
1 Most people cope well just by coughing.
2 Assess responsiveness, maintain an open airway and assess the victim's breathing. Start CPR if needed.
3 Advise the victim to seek medical help *immediately* if breathing difficulty occurs within 72 hours.
4 Treat for shock.
5 Arrange for transportation to hospital if coughing continues or breathing or level of consciousness is a problem.

Asthma
Asthma is a breathing disorder in which the airway's sensitivity is increased. This sensitivity results in spasms of the muscles of the airway (and therefore a narrowing of the airway) and increased production of mucus (and therefore a blockage of the airway).

People with asthma are likely to have specific "triggers" to the condition. Common triggers include allergies, emotional distress, and extreme temperatures.

Signs and Symptoms
✓ Difficulty breathing
✓ Anxiety
✓ Wheezing

Treatment
1 Assist the victim to a comfortable position. This often involves sitting and leaning forward slightly or standing and leaning forward with the arms resting on some object.
2 Help the victim take any medication he or she has.
3 Loosen tight-fitting clothing around the neck or chest.
4 Assist or encourage the victim in pursed-lip breathing.
5 Treat for shock.
6 If the asthma attack continues or is severe, arrange for transportation to hospital by contacting EMS.

Hyperventilation

Hyperventilation, sometimes called overbreathing, occurs when breathing is faster or deeper than necessary. Hyperventilation decreases the level of carbon dioxide in the blood, causing the body to depress the breathing centre in the brain. This can result in loss of consciousness.

How serious hyperventilation is depends on where it occurs. Loss of consciousness that occurs on land is usually temporary, as the carbon dioxide level in the blood flowing to the brain normalizes (unless additional injury results from a fall when the victim loses consciousness). But if loss of consciousness occurs underwater, the risk of drowning and aspiration is serious.

Voluntary hyperventilation is extremely dangerous and *should not be practised.*

Signs and Symptoms
✓ High rate of respiration, panting
✓ Lightheadedness, weakness, headache
✓ Tingling of hands, feet, and the area around the mouth
✓ Confusion, unconsciousness

Treatment
1 Assess responsiveness, maintain an open airway and assess the victim's breathing. Start CPR if needed.
2 Assist or encourage pursed-lip breathing.
3 Treat for shock.
4 Arrange for transportation to hospital if breathing problems are severe or ongoing or there is a decreased level of consciousness.

Respiratory Distress

Several unrelated medical conditions can cause respiratory distress. Conditions causing this distress include emphysema and chronic bronchitis (chronic obstructive lung diseases), pneumothorax (abnormal pressure in the lungs), and collapsed lungs.

Signs and Symptoms
✓ Difficulty breathing
✓ Anxiety
✓ Cyanosis
✓ Shock

Treatment

Treatment is as for hyperventilation, above:

1   Assess responsiveness, maintain an open airway and assess the victim's breathing. Start CPR if needed.
2   Assist or encourage pursed-lip breathing.
3   Treat for shock.
4   Arrange for transportation to hospital if breathing problems are severe or ongoing or there is a decreased level of consciousness.

8.4   Circulatory Disorders

Angina

Angina is a medical disorder caused by poor blood circulation to the heart. The heart muscle is having what might be considered muscle pain or muscle spasm.

Victims of angina often wear a necklace, bracelet, etc., identifying a medical condition. Known angina victims also usually carry medication for its treatment. Angina usually responds to treatment, but EMS assistance *is* required.

Signs and Symptoms

✓ Pain, pressure, or tightness in the chest or shoulder
✓ Trouble breathing, shortness of breath
✓ Flushed face, sweating
✓ Anxiety, fear
✓ Shock

Treatment

1   Assess responsiveness, maintain an open airway and assess the victim's breathing. Start CPR if needed.
2   Contact EMS.
3   Assist the victim into a comfortable position. This is often a semi-sitting position.
4   Help the victim take his or her angina medication as per the physician's directions. Encourage the victim to chew 1 adult or 2 children's ASA (e.g., Aspirin), unless the victim is allergic to ASA or has known upper or lower gastro-intestinal problems.
5   Loosen tight clothing around the neck and chest.
6   Treat for shock.
7   Give oxygen if you are trained to do so and it is both medically necessary and available.

Semi-sitting position

Heart Attack

Heart attack, sometimes called myocardial infarction, is a medical condition where the circulation of blood to the heart is severely affected. The severity of the heart attack and the damage to the heart muscle depend on the duration of the interruption in blood flow to the heart and the extent of the muscle affected.

Signs and Symptoms
✓ Pain, pressure, or tightness in the chest or shoulder
✓ Pain in the arms, neck, back, or jaw
✓ Trouble breathing, shortness of breath
✓ Flushed face, sweating
✓ Anxiety, fear
✓ Weak, rapid pulse
✓ Denial of symptoms
✓ Shock
✓ Confusion
✓ Nausea and weakness

Treatment
1 Assess responsiveness, maintain an open airway and assess the victim's breathing. Start CPR if needed.
2 Contact EMS.
3 Assist the victim into a comfortable position. This is often a semi-sitting position.
4 Help the victim take his or her angina medication as per the physician's directions. Encourage the victim to chew 1 adult or 2 children's ASA (e.g., Aspirin), unless the victim is allergic to ASA or has known upper or lower gastro-intestinal problems.
5 Loosen tight clothing around the neck and chest.
6 Treat for shock.
7 Give oxygen if you are trained to do so and it is both medically necessary and available.

Cardiac Arrest
"Cardiac arrest" means the heart has stopped beating. The evidence is absent or abnormal breathing (gasping) and other signs of circulation such as skin colour or a pulse. Blood stops carrying oxygen to the brain, heart, lungs, and vital organs, and tissue damage begins. Tissue damage becomes *significant* after about four minutes.

Signs and Symptoms
✓ Unconsciousness, unresponsiveness
✓ Not breathing
✓ Shock
✓ Gradual onset (angina or heart attack) or sudden onset (no warning)

Treatment
1 Contact EMS.
2 Initiate CPR immediately (see pages 7-13 to 7-15).
3 Treat for shock.
4 Give oxygen if you are trained to do so and it is both medically necessary and available.

Stroke
Strokes, also known as cerebrovascular accidents (CVAs), occur when part of the brain has an insufficient supply of blood. Causes of this interruption in supply include blockage or bleeding.

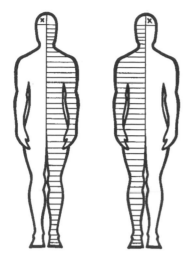

Nerve distribution from brain to body

The severity of a stroke (and the number of signs and symptoms) varies with the extent and location of the blockage of blood to the brain. For example, with mild blockage, the result might be mild arm or leg weakness on one side and decreased muscle co-ordination. And with more severe blockage, victims might be disoriented, lose control of their bowel or bladder, and be unable to move an arm or leg on one side. (Most nerves from one side of the body originate in the other side of the brain.)

Signs and Symptoms
✓ Gradual or sudden onset
✓ Head pain
✓ Lack of strength or co-ordination in the muscles in the arm and leg on one side of the body
✓ Facial problem on the side of the body opposite the area of the brain affected (facial muscle weakness, swallowing problems, drooling)
✓ Trouble understanding or speaking
✓ Unequal pupils
✓ Anxiety, agitation
✓ Decreased level of consciousness (confused, disoriented, unconscious)
✓ Loss of control of bowel or bladder
✓ Shock

Treatment
1 Assess responsiveness, maintain an open airway and assess the victim's breathing. Start CPR if needed.
2 Contact EMS.
3 Assist the victim into a comfortable position (often semi-sitting) or a recovery position if there are airway management problems.
4 Loosen tight clothing around the neck and chest.
5 Treat for shock.
6 Give oxygen if you are trained to do so and it is both medically necessary and available.

Transient Ischemic Attack (TIA)
A transient ischemic attack results in temporary stroke symptoms lasting less than twenty minutes. The signs and symptoms are similar to those for stroke and treatment is the same. Victims may be at risk for stroke. Encourage them to seek medical attention.

8.5   Bleeding

External Bleeding
Injury (trauma) to tissue can cause bleeding. The severity of the situation varies with the extent of the tissue damage and the amount of blood lost.

Skin tears (for example, skin sliced on metal) bleed, require treatment, and usually recover quickly. Facial cuts and head cuts and wounds result in more blood loss because of the number of blood vessels in the skin of the face and head.

Deep cuts and wounds may require stitches for tissue to heal. Cuts and wounds that involve bleeding from larger veins and arteries are more serious, and EMS must be called *promptly*.

The more blood the victim loses, the greater the extent of the shock.

Signs and Symptoms
✓ Blood
✓ Pain
✓ Distress, anxiety
✓ Shock

Treatment
1 One way to remember the treatment of severe bleeding is the 2 **P**s:
   ● **Position**: have the victim lay down to prevent further injury should he or she become unresponsive.
   ● **Pressure**: apply firm, direct pressure over the wound with the cleanest material available (a bandage, for example). Direct pressure is the most important factor in stopping blood flow. Secure direct pressure with a *tied* bandage. If blood starts to seep through the bandaging material, place a second bandage on top of the first. Do NOT lift the bandage—it interrupts the clotting of blood and increases bleeding.
2 Treat for shock.
3 Contact EMS if there is a lot of blood loss, if you cannot control the bleeding, or if moderate to severe shock becomes a factor.

Treatment of bleeding

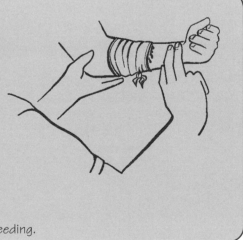

Bandaging Notes
❏ When securing bandages, tie the knot securely over the wound.
❏ Signs that a bandage is too tight include the part beyond the bandage getting cool, becoming pale, or lacking a pulse.
❏ When there is a foreign object in the wound, do NOT remove the object. Apply pressure around the object to avoid pushing it in deeper. The priority is to stop the bleeding.

Internal Abdominal Bleeding

Internal abdominal bleeding occurs when a trauma or medical disorder (ulcers, for example) causes bleeding into the abdominal tissues. Because the skin is intact, the blood pools *inside*. The severity of this condition varies with the amount and location of the bleeding.

Signs and Symptoms

✓ Abdominal muscle spasm or rigid abdomen
✓ Pain in the abdomen
✓ Difficulty breathing
✓ Shock
✓ Decreased level of consciousness
✓ Anxiety

Treatment

1 Assess responsiveness, maintain an open airway and assess the victim's breathing. Start CPR if needed.
2 Contact EMS.
3 Treat for shock.

Nosebleeds

Nosebleeds can be caused by trauma to the nose, or they can start spontaneously. Nosebleeds often look serious because of the amount of blood lost, but they usually respond promptly to treatment. Nosebleeds that last for more than a few minutes or recur in a short period of time may require medical attention.

Sign and Symptoms

✓ Blood from the nose
✓ Pain associated with the trauma (being hit, for instance)
✓ Anxiety
✓ Shock

Treatment

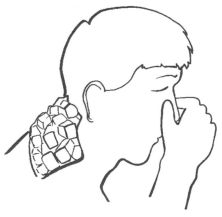

1 Pinch the nose where the soft nostril meets cartilage.
2 Treat for shock.
3 Apply ice to the forehead or the back of the neck.
4 Contact EMS if the nosebleed lasts more than a few minutes, if it recurs, or if the victim is in moderate to severe shock.

8.6   Trauma Injuries

Head Injuries

Head injuries occur when a force comes in contact with the head. This can happen when a victim's head hits an object or an object strikes the victim's head.

Head injuries need to be evaluated carefully. The bones of the head are quite strong and protective, but the brain tissues inside the skull are quite fragile. A seemingly minor head injury can have serious complications after a delay of several hours.

Whenever there is trauma to the head, you need to assess what area is probably affected:
❑ skin?
❑ bones?
❑ brain tissue?

The deeper the tissue affected, the more severe the injury.

A victim can have a brain injury even if no bones are broken. The brain is loose inside the skull, and shaking can damage the brain (just as you can shake a yolk in an egg without breaking the shell).

Significant trauma to the head can also cause damage to the upper spinal column. Such situations should be treated as a combined problem (head and neck injury).

Signs and Symptoms[†]
✓ Head pain
✓ Bleeding, swelling, or bruising at the site of the trauma
✓ Nausea and vomiting
✓ Decreased level of consciousness, confusion, disorientation, unconsciousness
✓ Anxiety, agitation
✓ Unequal, unreactive, fixed, or dilated pupils
✓ Shock
✓ Blood or clear fluid from the eyes, ears, nose, or mouth
† *Spinal-related signs and symptoms are covered on page 8-12.*

Treatment
1   Immobilize the head and neck in the position found unless breathing cannot be assessed.
2   Assess responsiveness, maintain an open airway and assess the victim's breathing. Start CPR if needed.
3   Contact EMS.
4   Treat the area of trauma for bleeding, bruising, or swelling.
5   Treat for shock.
6   Give oxygen if you are trained to do so and it is both medically necessary and available.

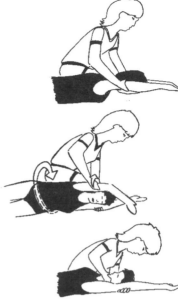

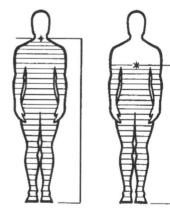

**Spinal rollover and
immobilization**

Spinal Injuries

Spinal injuries occur when trauma affects the nerves in the spinal column. Spinal injuries of the upper neck are often associated with head trauma and head injuries.

Most of the injury to the spinal cord occurs at the time of impact. Nevertheless, caution is essential to minimize further damage.

The part of the body affected depends on the level of the injury. Neck (or cervical) spinal injuries can affect the ability to swallow, breathe, or use the arms. Chest (or thoracic) spinal injuries can affect breathing, the chest wall, or internal organs. Low-back (or lumbar) spinal injuries can affect the bowel, bladder, or legs.

> **Spinal Injuries**
> Here are some common causes of spinal injuries:
> ❑ diving head-first into shallow water and hitting the bottom
> ❑ being thrown into the water
> ❑ diving into a sandbar
> ❑ making aggressive contact in water polo
> ❑ falls
> ❑ severe head injuries
> ❑ car accidents
> ❑ bicycle accidents.

See Section 5.10 for additional information on spinal rescue procedures.

* Injury site

Signs and Symptoms
✓ Pain at the site of the trauma
✓ Loss of co-ordination, sensation, or movement in parts beyond the injury
✓ Weakness or altered sensation usually affecting both sides of the body (both feet, for instance, or both arms)
✓ Bruising, swelling, or bleeding at the site of the trauma
✓ Shock

Treatment
1 If the victim is face down or partially submerged, roll the victim over using one of the rollover and immobilization techniques described on pages 5-14 to 5-17.
2 Assess responsiveness, maintain an open airway (see Jaw Thrust Technique, page 5-18) and assess the victim's breathing. Start CPR if needed.
3 Immobilize the head and body in proper alignment (see page 5-14) by packing the head and neck with such things as rolled towels, sandbags, or books.
4 If you are trained to do so and a spinal board is available, immobilize the victim on the board (see pages 5-19 to 5-21).
5 Treat the trauma site if there is bleeding (see Section 8.5).
6 Contact EMS.
7 Treat for shock.

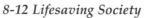

Chest Wounds

Chest wounds include injuries to the chest wall or ribs. These injuries can include bruising, fractures, and bleeding wounds. Common causes include falls, collisions, and blows from blunt objects.

Signs and Symptoms
✓ Trauma at the site of the injury (swelling, bruising, or bleeding)
✓ Pain at the site of the injury
✓ Difficulty in breathing
✓ Cyanosis of the lips and fingernails
✓ Shock

Treatment
1 Assess responsiveness, maintain an open airway and assess the victim's breathing. Start CPR if needed.
2 Treat the injury site for bleeding, bruising, etc.
3 Contact EMS.
4 Protect and support the injured area.
5 Treat for shock.
6 Give oxygen if you are trained to do so and it is both medically necessary and available.

Injuries from Embedded Objects

Occasionally an object gets "stuck" in a wound. This requires additional consideration beyond treatment of the specific injury. It is generally advisable to treat the wound *with the object in the wound* (for instance, glass in a cut or metal in a wound). If the embedding is superficial — as it is with splinters, for example — removing the object with a clean instrument is acceptable.

Signs and Symptoms
✓ Object protruding from or embedded in a wound
✓ Bleeding
✓ Pain
✓ Swelling, redness
✓ Shock

Treatment

1 Leave the object in place.
2 Control bleeding, stabilize the object to prevent further damage, and bandage the wound.
3 Contact EMS.
4 Treat for shock.
5 If the embedding is superficial, remove the object with a clean instrument (a needle or tweezers, for example), and treat the wound for bleeding (see Section 8.5) or other local injury.

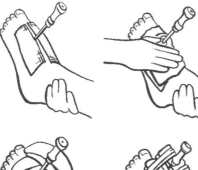

Bites

Bites by humans, animals, and insects often require first aid. If the victim has an allergy or sensitivity to the specific type of bite, anaphylaxis may be an issue (see page 8-3). For most bites, treatment of the injury site is the primary issue.

Signs and Symptoms
(for localized injury due to bites)

✓ Localized pain
✓ Bleeding
✓ Bruising, redness
✓ Puncture-type lacerations in the skin
✓ Shock

Treatment
(for localized injury due to bites)

1 Control bleeding.
2 Seek medical assistance (to have the risk of infection and immunization needs evaluated).
3 Treat for shock.

Eye Injuries

Because of the sensitive nature of the eye, you must take special care when treating injuries to or around the eye. The injury could be due to a foreign object such as chemicals in the eye.

Signs and Symptoms

✓ Pain in or around the eye
✓ Swelling, redness, bleeding, burning, or other injury
✓ Anxiety
✓ Shock

Treatment

1 Treat for shock.
2 Do not remove a foreign object manually or take any action that would embed an object deeper.
3 If a foreign object is floating in the eye, try flushing the eye with water.
4 If chemicals are the cause of the eye injury, flush the eye with running water for a long time — 15 to 20 minutes.
5 Contact EMS if there is an object in the eye or vision is affected.
6 If the eye area is wounded, treat the injury (for instance, a cut).
7 Bandage the injured eye by placing a patch bandage over it and securing the bandage.

8.7   Burns

Causes of burns include heat, chemicals, and electricity. Burns are classified in several ways. This section classifies them in terms of the depth of the skin affected: first-degree burns, second-degree burns, and third-degree burns. First-degree burns are the least serious, third-degree burns the most serious.

Burns to small children and infants are considered more serious because of the greater risk of shock. Burns to the neck and face require special attention because of the possible effect on breathing function.

First-Degree Burns

First-degree burns are those in which damage is restricted to the surface of the skin. First-degree burns can be quite painful; in cases such as sunburn, these burns can also be widespread.

Signs and Symptoms
✓ Redness
✓ Pain
✓ Mild swelling
✓ Anxiety
✓ Shock

Treatment

1 Assess responsiveness, maintain an open airway and assess the victim's breathing. Start CPR if needed.
2 Flush the burned area with cool, clean water or apply cold (not ice).
3 Repeat the flushing until the victim notes that the heat in the affected area has subsided.

> **Chemical Burns**
> ❑ Do not touch chemical products or the container they are in.
> ❑ Brush dry chemicals carefully to avoid a chemical cloud that can be inhaled.
> ❑ Since clothes can absorb chemicals, they should be removed or flushed with water.
> ❑ Remove the victim's shoes and socks—they can act as reservoirs for chemicals.
> ❑ Use large volumes of water to flush these burns.

4 Treat for shock.
5 Contact EMS if the area burned is large, the face and neck are affected, the victim is a small child or infant, or moderate to severe shock is a factor.

Second-Degree Burns

Second-degree burns affect the upper layers of skin. These burns are characterized by blisters, redness, pain, and swelling.

Signs and Symptoms
✓ Blisters
✓ Redness
✓ Pain
✓ Mild swelling
✓ Anxiety
✓ Shock

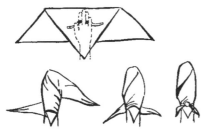

Bandaging burned fingers

Treatment
1 Assess responsiveness, maintain an open airway and assess the victim's breathing. Start CPR if needed.
2 Flush the burned area with cool, clean water or apply cold (not ice).
3 Repeat the flushing until any heat in the affected area subsides.
4 Apply a dry sterile dressing to the wound.
5 If the hands and feet are affected, separate the fingers or toes with dressings.
6 Treat for shock.
7 Contact EMS if the area burned is large, the face and neck are affected, the victim is a small child or infant, or moderate to severe shock is a factor.

Third-Degree Burns

Third-degree burns (also called "full-thickness burns") affect *all* the layers of tissue. Because the burn goes *through the skin*, the muscles, nerves and bones in the area may also be affected.

Signs and Symptoms
✓ Pain
✓ Red, black, and grey tissue
✓ Underlying tissue and organs exposed (muscles, nerves, and bones, for example)
✓ Second- and first-degree burns in nearby areas
✓ Anxiety
✓ Shock

Treatment

1 Assess responsiveness, maintain an open airway and assess the victim's breathing. Start CPR if needed.
2 Contact EMS.
3 Flush the burned area with cool, clean water or apply cold (not ice).
4 Repeat the flushing until any heat in the affected area subsides.
5 Apply a dry sterile dressing to the wound.
6 If the hands and feet are affected, separate the fingers or toes with dressings.
7 Treat for shock.

Separating burned fingers

> **Electrical Burns**
> Electrical burns can occur in one of two ways: when a short circuit causes a spark or when an electrical current passes through the body (electrification). Electrical currents can cause death (electrocution). With these burns,
> ❑ make sure the current is OFF before touching the victim or the electrical source
> ❑ stand in a dry area
> ❑ if the current cannot be turned off, use a long, dry, non-conducting object (wood or plastic, for example) to separate the victim from the current
> ❑ look for wounds where electricity entered and exited the body.

8.8   Medical Disorders

Diabetic Emergencies

Hypoglycemia occurs when there is not enough sugar in the bloodstream. This condition is found mainly in people with diabetes and is associated with not eating enough, exercising too much, being under a lot of stress, or taking too much insulin.

Signs and Symptoms
✓ Pale, cold, clammy skin
✓ Restlessness, weakness
✓ Fear, anxiety
✓ Confusion, disorientation
✓ Weak, rapid pulse
✓ Shallow, rapid respiration
✓ Cyanosis of the lips and fingernails
✓ Bracelet, necklace, etc., identifying diabetic condition

> First aiders do not have to be able to tell the difference between hypoglycemia and hyperglycemia. Signs and symptoms may vary but first aid treatment is the same.

Hyperglycemia occurs when there is too much sugar in the bloodstream (because there isn't enough insulin in the body to carry sugar from the blood to the cells).

Signs and Symptoms
✓ Flushed, dry skin
✓ Drowsiness to unconsciousness
✓ Excessive thirst and urination
✓ Acetone smell (for example, nail polish remover) on breath

Treatment for Diabetic Emergencies
1 Assess responsiveness, maintain an open airway and assess the victim's breathing. Start CPR if needed.
2 Help the victim self-administer sugar, a sugary drink such as fruit juice, or candy such as a chocolate bar.
3 Treat for shock.
4 Contact EMS if the victim is unconscious or if a conscious victim does not improve after eating sugar.

Seizure Disorders
Seizures occur when there is abnormal electrical activity in the brain. Seizures can be associated with the medical disorder epilepsy, with high fevers, and with drug intoxication.

There are several types of seizures. Of these, only tonic-clonic can be considered emergencies. Other types of seizures are of concern only if they cause a loss of consciousness and the victim is in the water. In such cases, the focus must be on checking breathing and circulation, rather than managing the seizure.

Signs and Symptoms
✓ Loss of consciousness
✓ Arching of the back and rigidity in the body
✓ Contraction and relaxation of the muscles of the arms and legs
✓ Cyanosis of the lips and fingernails
✓ Loss of control of the bowel or bladder
✓ Confusion, disorientation, fatigue after seizure

Treatment
1 If the victim is in water, get his or her head out of water; *after* the seizure, remove the victim from the water.
2 If the victim is on land, clear objects from the surrounding area to prevent him or her from striking them and getting injured.

3 DO NOT place anything between the victim's teeth.
4 Contact EMS.
5 *After the seizure is over,*
- assess the victim for injuries
- assess responsiveness, maintain an open airway and assess the victim's breathing. Start CPR if needed.
- treat for shock.

Drowning

Whenever distressed swimmers, non-breathing victims, or other victims of drowning are rescued, they must be evaluated and treated.

Signs and Symptoms
✓ Coughing
✓ Anxiety
✓ Weakness
✓ Nausea, vomiting
✓ Rapid breathing
✓ Shock

Treatment
1 Assess responsiveness, maintain an open airway and assess the victim's breathing. Start CPR if needed.
2 Contact EMS.
3 Treat for shock.
4 Give oxygen if you are trained to do so and it is both medically necessary and available.

Water Intoxication

Water intoxication is a rare medical condition found in children less than a year old. The condition occurs when swallowed water changes the chemical balance in the body. This condition can occur several hours *after* the water is swallowed.

Young children should be carefully observed—it's important to decrease the risk of water intoxication by preventing them from swallowing water. Water intoxication can occur when young children are intentionally immersed, for example, in swimming classes. Intentional immersion should be avoided with young children.

Signs and Symptoms
✓ Restlessness, disorientation
✓ Lethargy, weakness
✓ Gastric distension
✓ Nausea, vomiting
✓ Seizures

> The drowning process may result in Acute Respiratory Distress some hours after the initial drowning event and rescue. After rescue from the water, the victim should be sent to hospital if he or she:
> • suffered any loss of consciousness
> • required resuscitation (rescue breathing, CPR)
> • has any concurrent condition (e.g. seizure, spinal injury, asthma)
> • has on-going coughing

> **CPR and the Drowning Victim**
> The most detrimental consequence of submersion is hypoxia — lack of adequate oxygen. If the victim has been pulled from the water, open the airway, check for breathing and start CPR with rescue breaths before initiating compressions.

Treatment
1 Assess responsiveness, maintain an open airway and assess the victim's breathing. Start CPR if needed.
2 Contact EMS.
3 Treat for shock.

Fainting

Fainting is a temporary loss of consciousness. It is associated with several medical disorders, stress, fatigue, and shock.

Signs and Symptoms
✓ Pale, cool, clammy skin
✓ Restlessness, weakness
✓ Fear, anxiety
✓ Confusion, disorientation
✓ Weak, rapid pulse
✓ Shallow, rapid respiration

Treatment
1 Assess responsiveness, maintain an open airway and assess the victim's breathing. Start CPR if needed.
2 Identify and control the cause of the fainting.
3 Treat for shock.

Poisoning

This section refers to *ingested*, or *swallowed*, poisons. Ingested poisons include spoiled or contaminated food, medications or drugs, cleaning agents, and plants.

Rescuers should avoid contact with caustic agents. When assessing whether to induce vomiting, *consider the poison.* Read the instructions on the original container's label—it will provide directions for treatment. Caustic poisons that burn the passages to the lungs and stomach when swallowed probably do the same during vomiting; in such cases, do NOT induce vomiting.

Signs and Symptoms
✓ Abdominal pain or cramps
✓ Reduced level of consciousness
✓ Cyanosis of the lips and fingernails
✓ Coughing, difficulty breathing
✓ Vomiting
✓ Rash, blisters
✓ Changes in behavior, hallucinations, agitation, drowsiness
✓ Headache

Poisoning

Poisoning can also occur in these three ways:

❑ inhalation. Inhaled poisons include chlorine gas, chemical product powders and vapors, and carbon monoxide. See pages 8-5 and 8-6, on respiratory distress; for information on chlorine gas, see page 8-21.

❑ contact and absorption. Contacted and absorbed poisons include chemicals used for pool-water maintenance, insecticides, herbicides, fertilizers, and plants (poison oak and poison ivy, for example). Treat this form of poisoning as a burn (see Section 8.7).

❑ injection. Injected poisons include stings and bites (from insects or marine life, for example), medication, or non-prescription drugs. See page 8-14 for information on how to treat bites.

Treatment

1 Assess responsiveness, maintain an open airway and assess the victim's breathing. Start CPR if needed.
2 Contact EMS.
3 Contact the Poison Information Centre for assistance. (Check the front pages of your telephone book for the local number.)
4 Induce vomiting *if the original product label recommends it*.
5 Treat for shock.
6 Give oxygen if you are trained to do so and it is both medically necessary and available.
7 If hazardous material has been spilled, call the fire department.
8 Whenever possible, put the poison and its container in a clear plastic bag. Note the name of the poison, and give that information and the poison container to EMS.

If There's a Chlorine Gas Leak . . .

✓ Clear the water area and all areas near the leak by moving swimmers upwind from the source of the leak.
✓ Evacuate the facility, staying upwind of the gas source.
✓ Contact EMS.
✓ Treat victims for respiratory difficulties, apply resuscitation measures as needed, and monitor victims' vital signs.
✓ If you are trained to do so, put on a self-contained air pack, turn off the source of the gas, and remove to safety any victims who have collapsed.
✓ Treat for shock.
✓ Refer anyone who inhaled chlorine gas to medical attention.

If the gas leaking is a heavy gas, stay as upright as you can.

8.9   Heat/Cold Disorders

Heat Cramps

Heat cramps are caused by the dehydration and salt depletion associated with excessive sweating. Heat cramps are characterized by painful cramps in large muscles.

Signs and Symptoms
✓ Pain and spasms in muscles
✓ Cool, clammy skin (sweating)
✓ Fatigue, dizziness, headache
✓ Nausea
✓ Shock

Treatment
1. Remove the victim from the hot environment.
2. Give the victim cool water or a sport drink (e.g., Gatorade) if available.
3. Stretch the cramp.
4. Advise the victim to eat well to restore the depleted body salt.
5. Treat for shock.

Heat Exhaustion

Heat exhaustion can occur when a person is exposed to high temperatures for a long time. Water loss occurs through perspiration and *can* result in mineral and salt loss.

Signs and Symptoms
✓ Nausea
✓ Headache, dizziness
✓ Pale, cool, clammy skin (sweating)
✓ Restlessness, weakness
✓ Fear, anxiety
✓ Confusion, disorientation
✓ Weak, rapid pulse
✓ Shallow, rapid respiration
✓ Cyanosis of the lips and fingernails

Treatment
1. Remove the victim from the hot environment.
2. If the victim is alert and nausea is not a problem, give him or her cool water or a sport drink (e.g., Gatorade) if available.
3. Advise the victim to eat well to restore the depleted body salt.
4. Treat for shock.
5. Contact EMS if the victim's level of consciousness is decreased or moderate to severe shock is a factor.

Heatstroke

Heatstroke is a rare but serious condition in which the body's cooling mechanism stops working. The body's core temperature starts to rise, and the body organs are at risk of tissue damage, convulsions (tonic-clonic seizures; see page 8-18), and cardiac arrhythmia. Those most likely to suffer heatstroke are young children and infants, the elderly, and cardiac patients.

Signs and Symptoms
✓ Fever
✓ Hot, dry skin, flushed face
✓ Nausea, vomiting
✓ Full, pounding pulse
✓ Decreased level of consciousness (confused, disoriented, unconscious)
✓ Seizures

> **Alcohol and Heat/Cold Disorders**
> Alcohol accelerates and worsens the effect of heat or cold—it stimulates blood vessel dilation at the skin's surface, which speeds up heat loss. This means that the body's ability to adjust its core temperature up or down is further compromised. Those being treated for heat- or cold-related difficulties should NOT drink alcoholic beverages!

Treatment
1 Assess responsiveness, maintain an open airway and assess the victim's breathing. Start CPR if needed.
2 Contact EMS.
3 Remove the victim from the hot environment.
4 Remove the outer layer of the victim's clothing.
5 Cool the victim's body core (head, neck, chest, back and groin) by wrapping him or her in wet sheets or fanning the body. If the victim is alert, walk him or her into cool water up to the knees. Ask the victim to sit down so he or she is immersed up to the shoulders.
6 Treat for shock.

> **Be Sun Smart**
> Overexposure to the sun can be extremely dangerous. In the short run, unprotected exposure can cause moderate to severe sunburn. In the long run, the skin and eyes can be damaged. The risk of skin cancer and cataracts increases with exposure.
>
> Suntans and sunburns are both signs of skin damage. Even after a sunburn heals, the damage remains and increases with each burn.
>
> Reflections from water, sand, and concrete can intensify the effect of the sun's rays. Even on overcast days, sunscreen is necessary, because the sun's ultraviolet (UV) radiation is still present. Everyone doing aquatic activities outdoors should take Sun-Smart precautions:
> ✓ Wear clothing that covers exposed skin.
> ✓ Wear a hat that protects the face and the back of the neck.
> ✓ Use sunscreen with a sun protection factor (SPF) of at least 15.
> ✓ Apply sunscreen and lip balm to protect exposed skin. Apply and reapply sunscreen according to the manufacturer's directions.
> ✓ Wear protective sunglasses.
> ✓ If appropriate, wear a wetsuit or other protective clothing to prevent sunburn or wind chill.
> ✓ Monitor UV ratings and forecasts in weather reports.

Frostbite

Frostbite is freezing that occurs in external tissue. The tissue most at risk is exposed skin (usually the ears and face), fingers, and toes.

Signs and Symptoms
✓ Pain
✓ Altered sensation (burning sensation, pins and needles, numbness)
✓ White area on the skin

Treatment
1 Remove the victim from the cold environment.
2 Reheat the affected area with body heat (for instance, put frostbitten fingers under the armpits, or cup the frostbitten face or ears in the hands) or immerse the affected body part in warm water.

So What Do You Mean by Cold Water?

Many factors affect how your body responds to cold water. Here are some of them:

❑ length of time in the water
❑ water temperature
❑ amount of body fat
❑ amount of the body that is submerged
❑ whether clothing or a lifejacket is worn
❑ body position
❑ age.

Water temperatures as warm as 20° Celsius are considered a risk for hypothermia.

Hypothermia

Hypothermia refers to a dropping of the body's core temperature. This medically serious condition can occur with exposure to cold water or air. Most of Canada's lakes, streams, rivers, and oceans are cold year-round; hypothermia can therefore happen *any time of year*. (For more information on hypothermia, see page 2-6.)

Signs and Symptoms
✓ Shivering, feeling cold
✓ Loss of muscular co-ordination
✓ Decreased consciousness, confusion, disorientation, unconsciousness
✓ Fatigue
✓ Shock

Treatment
1 Assess responsivenss, maintain an open airway and assess the victim's breathing. Start CPR if needed.
2 Contact EMS.
3 Remove the victim from the cold environment.
4 Warm the victim's body core (head, neck, chest, back, and groin) by giving warm beverages if the victim is alert, wrapping him or her in warm blankets, or getting into the huddle position.
5 Treat for shock.
6 Give oxygen if you are trained to do so and it is both medically necessary and available.

8.10   Bone, Joint, and Soft-Tissue Disorders

Bruising

Bruising occurs when tissue or muscle bleeds below the skin. Bruising is usually associated with trauma (being hit, for instance).

Signs and Symptoms
✓ Pain
✓ Redness and blueness in the affected area
✓ Mild swelling

Treatment
1 Ice the injured part for 10 to 15 minutes every hour until the swelling subsides.

Sprains and Strains

Sprains and strains both refer to stretching or tearing of muscle, tendons, or ligaments. Soft-tissue injuries (injuries to muscles, tendons, or ligaments) can occur during physical activity or by trauma (falls, hits, etc.).

Signs and Symptoms
✓ Pain
✓ Swelling
✓ Discoloration (bruising)
✓ Difficulty moving the affected area

Treatment
1 The way to remember treatment of sprains and strains is the word RICE:
   ● *Rest*. Rest the injured part.
   ● *Immobilize*. Immobilize the injured part in a comfortable position - *don't* move it!
   ● *Cold*. Ice the injured part for 10-15 minutes every hour until the swelling subsides. Icing is *the most important component* of treatment.
   ● *Elevate*. Elevate the injured part — it helps control swelling.
2 Contact EMS.
3 Treat for shock.

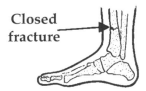

Closed Fractures

Closed fractures are breaks in a bone. *Undisplaced closed fractures* are like a crack in a teacup—there's a break in the surface but not in alignment. Undisplaced fractures can be distinguished from sprains and strains only on X-rays. *Displaced fractures* are fractures in which there's a break in the surface *and* in alignment.

Closed fracture

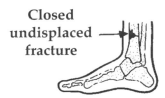

Closed undisplaced fracture

Signs and Symptoms
✓ Pain
✓ Swelling
✓ Discoloration
✓ Difficulty moving the affected area

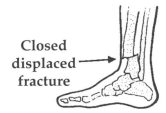

Closed displaced fracture

Treatment

1 The way to remember treatment of simple fractures is the word RICE:

- *Rest*. Rest the injured part.
- *Immobilize*. Immobilize the injured part in a comfortable position—*don't* move it!
- *Cold*. Ice the injured part for 10-15 minutes every hour until the swelling subsides. Icing is *the most important component* of treatment.
- *Elevate*. Elevate the injured, splinted part (it helps control swelling) but not if it increases pain, discomfort or harm.

2 Contact EMS.

3 Treat for shock.

4 Assess the pulse and movement beyond the site of the injury. For instance, assess the pulse and movement in the ankle if the leg is broken.

> ### Immobilization
> ✓ To immobilize a hand, wrist, arm, elbow, or shoulder, you can use an arm sling.
> ✓ To immobilize a wrist, ankle, or foot, you can use a pillow or towel to splint.
>
> ✓ To immobilize joints, you can use air splints, wooden splints, or splints made out of cardboard or rolled newspaper.

Open Fractures

Open fractures are displaced fractures in which a bone breaks through the skin. *Unless it is absolutely essential*, do NOT move victims with this condition—it could cause further muscle and nerve damage.

Signs and Symptoms

✓ Pain
✓ Swelling
✓ Bone protruding through the skin
✓ Bleeding
✓ Discoloration
✓ Difficulty moving the affected part

Treatment

1 Rest the affected part, and immobilize it *as you found it*. Do *not* attempt realignment.

2 Place a clean bandage over the exposed bone.

3 Ice the injury for 10 to 15 minutes. *Avoid wetting the open wound*.

4 Contact EMS.

5 Treat for shock.

Dislocations

A dislocation is an injury in which the bones at a joint are displaced from their usual alignment. The joints most commonly dislocated are shoulders, fingers, and toes.

Signs and Symptoms
✓ Pain
✓ Swelling
✓ Discoloration
✓ Difficulty moving the affected area

Treatment
1 Rest the injured part. Immobilize it in a comfortable position—*don't* move it!
2 Ice the injured part for 10 to 15 minutes every hour.
3 Support the injured part in a position of comfort.
4 Contact EMS.
5 Treat for shock.

Muscle Cramps

Muscle cramps (sometimes called charley horses) are spasms in the muscle. They can occur because of loss of body salt (see the information on heat cramps on pages 8-21 and 8-22) or as a reaction to cold air or water. Not warming up enough before activity can also lead to muscle cramps.

Signs and Symptoms
✓ Pain in the muscle
✓ Muscle twitching or spasms

Treatment
1 Stretch the muscle (*slowly* lengthen the muscle fibres).
2 Gently massage along the length of the muscle.
3 Apply mild heat (warm shower or warm, wet cloth).

8.11 Scuba-Diving and Skin-Diving Disorders

Scuba-diving and skin-diving disorders include squeezes, air embolism, and decompression sickness. Some of these conditions occur because people don't take necessary precautions, for example, in dives or entries.

In scuba-diving and skin-diving disorders, victims' signs and symptoms often mirror those of other medical disorders. *Treat the medical disorder you find in your assessment.* Also, be sure to advise EMS that the condition is related to scuba diving or skin diving.

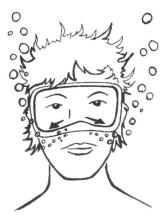

Equalizing pressure

Squeezes

Squeezes result from the increasing pressure water exerts on a body as it descends. Water exerts pressure on air spaces in the body: ears, sinuses, cavities, and lungs. Water also exerts pressure on equipment such as masks.

Signs and Symptoms
✓ Severe pressure pain in the affected area

Treatment
1 Ascend for a short distance, and try to equalize pressure.
2 With mask squeezes, blow gently through the nose.
3 If the squeeze occurs during a dive, initiate your established procedures for ending the dive.
4 If the pain persists, contact EMS.

Air Embolism

An air embolism is an air bubble in the bloodstream. Holding the breath or ascending faster than its bubbles are rising may lead to this condition. Air bubbles may escape from the lungs, block small arteries and capillaries, and prevent blood flow to the heart or brain.

Signs and Symptoms
✓ Fast onset during ascent
✓ Weakness, dizziness
✓ Paralysis, change in vision
✓ Chest pain, blood in mouth
✓ Convulsions
✓ Unconsciousness
✓ Stoppage in breathing

Treatment
1 Assess responsiveness, maintain an open airway and assess the victim's breathing. Start CPR if needed.
2 Give oxygen if you are trained to do so and it is both medically necessary and available.
3 Treat for shock.
4 Call EMS, advise them that the emergency is related to scuba diving or skin diving, and make arrangements for transport to a decompression chamber.

Decompression Sickness

In decompression sickness, also known as "the bends," small pockets of nitrogen form in the body tissues and blood. This condition is most likely to occur after a long, deep dive — deeper than you can do in most pools. Decompression sickness is also associated with surfacing too fast.

Signs and Symptoms

✓ Pain
✓ When nitrogen bubbles go to the brain
  ● blindness, dizziness
  ● paralysis, convulsions
  ● unconsciousness
✓ When nitrogen bubbles go to the joints, muscles, or bones
  ● pain
  ● blocked circulation
✓ When nitrogen bubbles go to the spinal cord
  ● paralysis
  ● loss of feeling
✓ When nitrogen bubbles go to the lungs
  ● labored breathing
  ● coughing
  ● burning chest pain
✓ When nitrogen bubbles go to the skin
  ● itch, rash

Treatment

1 Assess responsiveness, maintain an open airway and assess the victim's breathing. Start CPR if needed.
2 Call EMS, advise them that the emergency is related to scuba diving or skin diving, and make arrangements for transport to a decompression chamber.
3 Treat for shock.

8.12   Want to Know More?

American Heart Association, *Circulation*, Volume 122, Issue 18_suppl_3; November 2, 2010. Presents 2010 American Heart Association Guidelines for Cardiopulmonary Resuscitation and Emergency Cardiovascular Care Science. Visit: www.circ.ahajournals.org.

Christensen, Anna, editor. *Wilderness First Aid*. Vancouver: Wilderness First Aid and Safety Association, 1986.
> This comprehensive manual is a wealth of information. It covers a variety of injuries in considerable detail and also explores related topics such as legal issues.

La fédération française d'études et de sports sous-marins. *Plongée, santé, sécurité*, third edition. Éditions Ouest-France, n.d.
> This text presents a detailed examination of medical conditions that may result while scuba diving. It also describes the circumstances that contribute to them. The text stresses the safety practices that divers should follow.

Huint, Richard. *Understanding Drowning (and Related Topics)*. Montreal: AquaLude Inc., 1992.
> This text presents detailed information on the physiology of drowning and summarizes significant scientific research on the subject. It is of particular interest to lifeguards and aquatics instructors.

Lifesaving Society. *Alert: Lifeguarding in Action*. Ottawa: Royal Life Saving Society Canada, 1993.
> *Alert* is the text of the National Lifeguard Service. Designed for professional lifeguards, *Alert* presents information on accident prevention and rescue skills and procedures.

Lifesaving Society. *Canadian First Aid Manual*. Toronto: First edition, April 2005, ninth printing, revised, November 2011.
> The *Canadian First Aid Manual* is the comprehensive reference text for Lifesaving Society first aid training courses.

Lifesaving Society. *Ice: The Winter Killer: a resource manual about ice, ice safety and ice rescue*. Ottawa: Royal Life Saving Society Canada, 1998.
> Features ice-related drowning statistics; facts about ice, ice smart safety tips; signs and symptoms of cold shock response and hypothermia; ice rescue procedures; signs and symptoms of critical incident stress; steps to help communities promote ice safety.

Professional Association of Diving Instructors (PADI). *Open Water Dive Manual*. Santa Ana: PADI, 1988.
> This manual is about the fun and adventure of learning to scuba dive. A manual for candidates in PADI courses, *Open Water Dive Manual* presents information on scuba equipment, clothing, scuba safety, and the physiology and psychology of scuba diving. Information on how to use the decompression tables is also included.

Wilkinson, James, Cameron Bangs, and John Hayward. *Hypothermia, Frostbite and Other Cold Injuries*. Seattle: The Mountaineers, 1986.
> This is a short but comprehensive work on cold-related injuries and the complications associated with them. It contains an excellent chapter on immersion hypothermia.

Chapter 9
Rescue Strokes and Skills

9.1   Introduction

Lifesavers use swimming in self-rescue and the rescue of others. As a rescuer, you need to *apply* swimming principles and *adapt* stroke technique to your needs. This chapter presents strokes and skills *as lifesavers would use them*. Strokes and skills are both described in terms of maximum efficiency: how to get the most out of them with the least amount of energy.

9.2   Swimming Strokes

The following strokes are most useful to lifesavers:
✓ front crawl, head-up front crawl
✓ back crawl, back crawl for rescues
✓ breaststroke, head-up breaststroke.

The rest of this section describes these strokes in detail. In some cases, technical terms such as propulsion (forward movement) and resistance (drag) are used. These terms are discussed in Appendix C to this manual.

Front Crawl

Front crawl is the most efficient stroke. It keeps the body level at the surface. It also creates little frontal resistance, because the kick is shallow and the arms recover above the water. The long bent-arm pull of front crawl provides *continuous* propulsion.

Body and Head Position
✓ The body is on the front, streamlined, relaxed, and horizontal.
✓ Roll the body throughout the stroke along an imaginary line that runs down the middle of the body.
✓ Cradle the head with the waterline at the hairline and the eyes looking forward. If necessary, adjust body angle by changing your head position (for example, lowering the head raises the feet).

Leg Action
✓ The flutter kick balances and stabilizes the rolling swimmer. For many swimmers, this kick also levels the body. Those with proportionally stronger kicks can maintain good propulsion throughout the kick.

✓ The kick used depends on your need for stability. It may be a regular kick (for example, 3 downward beats to 1 arm pull). Or it may be an irregular or periodic kick. Choose a flutter kick that maintains body position and prevents side-to-side swaying.

✓ Kick the legs rhythmically, up and down, from the hips. Relax the legs so that the knees are slightly bent. The feet should be loose and relaxed.

Arm Action
✓ One arm pulls underwater while the other recovers above the surface. Try to alternate the arms *continuously*. The arms provide most of the forward movement in front crawl.

Drive. Drive in the arm action is as follows:
✓ The arm enters the water in front of its shoulder. The hand leads, thumb first, and is held comfortably at a 45° angle. The body rolls toward the arm as it extends in front.
✓ The hand pulls backward through an S-shaped pattern. The hand pushes inward until the hand is under the chest. The elbow bends increasingly until halfway through the pull. At this point, the elbow is bent at most 90°.
✓ As it passes the waist, the elbow extends. The hand pushes backward and outward past the side of the thigh. The thumb almost touches the thigh as the shoulder and wrist come out of the water. The elbow leads the recovery out of the water, and the hand follows.

Recovery. Recovery in the arm action is as follows:
✓ Reach forward into the water on the leading arm, and roll toward the arm as it pulls.
✓ Raise the shoulder of the recovering arm — it helps the arm clear the surface.
✓ The bent elbow is carried higher than the hand. The hand is as close to the body and the surface as is comfortable. (A wide recovery can lead to excessive sideways body movement.)
✓ The arm extends forward, returning to its entry position in front of the shoulder.

Breathing
✓ Exhale below the surface through the mouth and nose. Finish exhaling as the mouth clears the surface.
✓ Roll the head with the body, turning sideways just enough to allow inhalation. Inhale through the mouth or mouth and nose.
✓ Do *not* lift the head out of the water to breathe in or out.
✓ Breathing follows a regular pattern. You may breathe after every 2, 3, 4, or more strokes. Choose the breathing pattern that is most comfortable for you. (This pattern will depend on such things as what the water conditions are and how far you have to swim.)

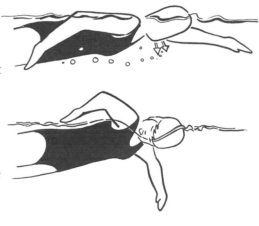

Co-ordination

✓ Since the recovery takes less time than the drive, one arm should enter as the other is about halfway through the drive. Individual variations may occur. These variations will depend on such factors as your swimming speed and your swimming background (sprinter or distance swimmer).

✓ Timing of the leg action should occur *naturally*. Tempo varies with the arm action.

✓ Maintain the kick's tempo even when your arms get tired.

Head-up Front Crawl

Lifesavers often use the head-up version of front crawl as they approach victims. This stroke allows you to keep the victim in view and to reach him or her quickly. Head-up front crawl is preferable to regular front crawl in cold water because it reduces heat loss from the head.

While the stroke is *almost* the same as regular front crawl, there are the following differences:

✓ The head is held up to provide an unrestricted view ahead. This causes the feet to sink.

✓ Use the breathing rhythm that is most comfortable for you.

✓ The knees are more bent in the kick, which is more vigorous than in regular front crawl. These changes compensate for the feet sinking.

✓ The arm stroke includes a downward push while pulling to help raise the head and keep it above water.

Back Crawl

Like the front crawl, back crawl uses an alternating arm action with recovery over the water, combined with a flutter kick.

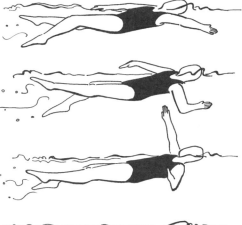

Body and Head Position

✓ The body is stretched on its back in a streamlined position. The hips are just below the surface.
✓ The head is held comfortably at the surface, in line with the body.
✓ The head is held steady as the body rolls about an imaginary line down the middle of the body.
✓ The eyes can focus on the ceiling, sky, or other "object" — it helps keep you on course.

Leg Action

The flutter kick is more important in back crawl than in front crawl. In addition to being needed for stability, this kick is needed for lift and propulsion. Here are the important features of flutter kick for back crawl:

✓ The knees flex more, but the kick still starts in the hips.
✓ The kick is done in a regular cycle (usually 3 upward beats to every arm pull).
✓ The toes — but no part of the leg — just break the surface.
✓ The ankles are relaxed, and the feet turn slightly inward.
✓ The upward beat of the kick is the driving part of the kick.

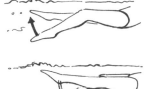

Arm Action

Drive. Drive in the arm action is as follows:

✓ The hand leads the extended arm into the water above and beside the head. Try to have the little finger enter the water first.

✓ The body rolls toward the extended arm. This pushes the hand below the surface. As the hand starts to pull, the elbow bends.

✓ The bent elbow points downward to the bottom (*not* to the feet). The elbow bend increases to *at most* 90° as the hand passes the shoulder.

✓ The hand pushes down and back in a curved or elongated S-shaped path. The elbow straightens near the end of the push. Water pressure is felt on the palm and the inner surface of the arm.

✓ The hand finishes with a vigorous push, palm downward. This starts a body roll away from that arm as the other arm enters the water.

Recovery. Recovery in the arm action is as follows:

✓ The arm recovers over the shoulder, which may lightly brush the cheek during the transition to the entry.

✓ The arm stays straight but relaxed, with the palm turning outward.

Breathing

✓ Breathing presents few problems, since the face is always above water.

✓ The breathing pattern should be regular.

Co-ordination

✓ As one arm finishes the drive, the other arm is ready to start the next propulsive phase.

Back Crawl for Rescues

You can use back crawl in rescues when you're using a towing assist with shoulder loops. Such assists include rescue cans, rescue tubes, and lifejackets.

Technique for this stroke is like that for back crawl, except that

✓ the head is raised so that you can see the victim

✓ the arm action may be shorter, with the arms entering farther away from the head

✓ flutter kick or eggbeater kick may be used:

● If the flutter kick is used, you don't have to make *any* changes in the kick.

● If eggbeater is used, time the stroke so that the left leg kicks while the right arm pulls. The right leg kicks while the left arm pulls.

● The body is almost in a sitting position.

> Using back crawl with a towing assist can be dangerous, because victims can pull you toward them and increase your chances of being grabbed. Practise getting out of the shoulder loop **fast**!

Breaststroke

Breaststroke is very useful in lifesaving because
✓ you can approach victims quickly *and* see well
✓ it is a survival skill in self-rescue
✓ you can easily adapt it for underwater swimming
✓ most swimmers find it a less tiring stroke than front crawl for long distances.

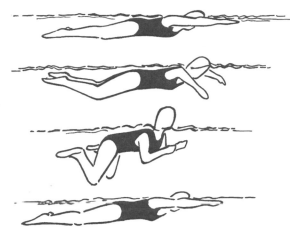

Body and Head Position
✓ Keep the body as horizontal as possible — it reduces resistance.
✓ Let the water support your head. Look forward, and lift the head during the arm stroke to breathe.

Leg Action
✓ In the position of full extension, the legs are extended, in line with the trunk, and just below the surface. The toes are pointed, the ankles relaxed.

Recovery. Recovery in the leg action is as follows:
✓ The legs recover from full extension by bending at the knees, hips, and ankles. This action starts naturally as the shoulders rise. The heels are drawn along the surface, toward the buttocks. The heels are close to — but do not break — the surface of the water.
✓ The toes turn outward, the ankles flex, and the knees separate to about shoulder width as they fully bend. The ankles continue to flex with the toes bent and pulled up toward the shins.

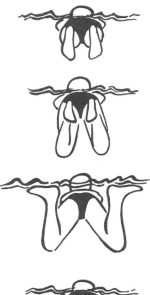

Drive. Drive in the leg action is as follows:
✓ The insides of the feet and legs face backward to provide the surface area for backward thrust.
✓ The drive starts when the feet are thrust apart and backward. The heels trace an arc pattern as they travel backward. Water pressure is felt on the insides of the legs and feet.
✓ The feet accelerate smoothly, reaching maximum speed at midstage in the kick.
✓ The knees extend, accelerating the feet. Since knee extension provides speed, the knees should finish their extension as the feet come together at the end of the kick.
✓ The feet come together momentarily, just after the legs straighten. The ankles and feet are loose.

Arm Action

Drive. Drive in the arm action is as follows:

✓ The pull starts with the arms pressing downward and outward in a diagonal motion. The hands are held at a 45° angle with the palms outward. The body and arms outline the letter "Y."

✓ The hands accelerate toward the centre line of the body. They are at a 45° angle with the palms inward.

✓ The elbows stay high until the hands finish the inward movement.

✓ The hands pull to the shoulder, but not past it.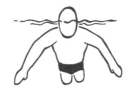

Recovery. Recovery in the arm action is as follows:

✓ The hands are together and slide forward to full arm extension beyond the head.

✓ The palms are pitched toward each other (thumb-side up). As the arms near full extension, the hands rotate (thumb-side down to 45°), ready for the next arm cycle.

Breathing

✓ Take a breath on every stroke as the arms start to move outward.

✓ Exhale below the surface.

✓ Extend the neck early in the arm stroke.

✓ Return the face to the water by the middle of the arm pull.

Co-ordination

Here's a sequence you can use to co-ordinate movement in this stroke:

✓ Pull.

✓ Breathe.

✓ Kick.

✓ Stretch.

Head-up Breaststroke

The head-up version of breaststroke is used to maintain eye contact while approaching victims in rescue situations. The head-up position gives you a clear view and reduces heat loss in cold water. While slower than head-up front crawl, this stroke is often less tiring over long distances. While the stroke is very similar to regular breaststroke, there are some differences:

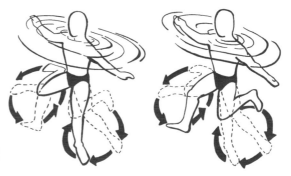

✓ The head is held high enough to stay above the water at all times and to allow the eyes a clear forward view.
✓ Because of the raised head, the legs are slightly deeper.
✓ The arm motion is modified to include pulling down to help raise the head and keep it above water.

9.3   Swimming Skills

This section covers a number of swimming skills used in lifesaving:
❏ lifesaving kicks
❏ sculling and finning
❏ surface dives
❏ underwater swimming.

Lifesaving Kicks

Lifesavers use various kicks to tow or carry victims to safety. You can also use these kicks to support yourself vertically, or you can modify them for use in underwater swims. Because of their uses in rescues, you need to practise these kicks without using your arms. These are the kicks:
❏ eggbeater kick
❏ whip kick
❏ scissor kick
❏ inverted scissor kick.

Eggbeater Kick

Eggbeater kick provides steady and powerful propulsion, and it is the most useful lifesaving kick for vertical support. Because it provides smooth propulsion, eggbeater is also the most useful kick for transporting victims with spinal injuries. It may be used with a variety of carries (see pages 4-20 to 4-24). In demanding water conditions, lifesavers often find they get "bounced around" with eggbeater, making kicks such as whip kick or scissor kick more useful in such situations.

Body Position for Vertical Support. Body position is as follows:

✓ Sit in the water with the back straight, the knees bent, the legs spread at the hips, and the thighs almost parallel to the water surface.

✓ Flex the feet at about 90° to the shins.

Leg Action. Leg action is as follows:

✓ The legs drive in a semi-circular pattern toward the midline of the body, with rotation about the knees.

✓ As one leg drives, the other recovers.

✓ The insides of the legs push water *down* on an angle as the insides of the feet slice through the water and the feet press and slide down and out from the midline of the body.

Eggbeater Kick in a Lifesaving Tow or Carry. Here's how to use eggbeater kick in a lifesaving tow or carry:

✓ To travel backward in the near-vertical position, lean back in the water, and adjust the leg position to push water in the direction opposite the line of travel.

✓ To travel while towing or carrying a victim, lean back into a semi-sitting position. Cradle the back of your head at the water surface. The nature of the kick causes some lowering of the hips.

Eggbeater Kick in Underwater Swims. The key points are as follows:

✓ For underwater swims, eggbeater can be performed on the front. There is less of a bend at the waist than for eggbeater on the back.

✓ Leg action is the same.

✓ For underwater searches, sweep the bottom with one arm, and protect your head with the other in murky water. Propulsion from the kick is enough to move you forward effectively even if you don't use your hands for movement.

Whip Kick

The whip kick is a powerful lifesaving kick. Because it provides a stop-start type of forward propulsion, it is less useful than eggbeater for vertical support or for transporting victims with spinal injuries. Whip kick may also be used with a variety of carries (see pages 4-20 to 4-24). It is especially effective with large or heavy victims and in adverse water conditions.

Body and Head Position. Start on the back with the hips at or just below the surface. Let the water support the head in line with the body.

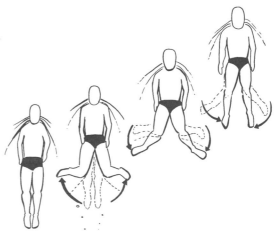

Leg Action. The key points of the recovery are as follows:
- ✓ The legs are together, fully extended at or just below the surface. The toes are pointed.
- ✓ The legs start to recover with the knees bending. This allows the lower legs to drop.
- ✓ As the heels are drawn toward the buttocks, the knees separate to about shoulder width. The feet are flexed at 90° to the shins. Throughout these actions, the body stays close to the horizontal.

Technique for the drive is as follows:
- ✓ Start the drive by thrusting the feet apart and tracing an arc pattern with the heels as the legs are extended. You will feel the water pressure on the insides of your legs and feet.
- ✓ Accelerate the feet smoothly, reaching maximum speed at the kick's midstage.
- ✓ As the feet accelerate, extend the knees. This extension provides speed; so complete the extension of the knees only when the feet are coming together at the end of the kick.
- ✓ Bring the feet together in a momentary pause, just after the legs straighten. Point the toes.
- ✓ Start the recovery as soon as the drive is finished. This will minimize jerkiness.
- ✓ Make sure the recovery is gentle, the drive vigorous.

Breathing. Inhale during the recovery, and exhale during the drive.

Scissor Kick

Lifesavers who have trouble with eggbeater or whip kick do have alternatives. Scissor kick may be preferable for lifesavers with knee problems. Its forward movement is not continuous, and it can create a lot of frontal resistance in the recovery phase. It is therefore not as useful for vertical support or transporting victims with spinal injuries. Rescuers using the scissor kick during carries must make a conscious effort to avoid or minimize kicking victims.

Body and Head Position. The key points are as follows:
- ✓ The body is stretched out on its side in a relaxed and streamlined position, as horizontal as possible.
- ✓ The head is cradled on its side in a position of maximum buoyancy. The head and upper body may twist toward the back.

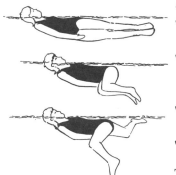

Leg Action. Recovery in the leg action is as follows:

✓ Start the kick by bending at the hips and knees with the legs and feet together.

✓ Recover the legs together, and keep them in front of the trunk to reduce resistance. Some leg separation may be necessary to avoid kicking victims.

✓ Extend the top leg *forward* with the ankle flexed (toes drawn up toward the shin) until the legs are straight.

✓ Extend the bottom leg *backward* with the toes pointed.

The key points in the drive are as follows:

✓ Drive the legs backward. Water pressure is felt against the sole of the top foot and the upper surface of the bottom foot.

✓ The legs are held together for a short pause in a streamlined position. The toes are pointed.

Breathing. Inhale during the recovery, and exhale during the drive.

Inverted Scissor Kick

Inverted scissor kick may also be preferable for lifesavers with knee problems. It has fewer limitations than scissor kick, but more than eggbeater or whip kick. As in scissor kick, propulsion is not continuous, and the kick creates a lot of frontal resistance in its recovery phase. The kick is therefore not very useful for vertical support or for the transporting of victims with spinal injuries. Unlike scissor kick, the inverted kick can be used with most carries because the top leg recovers *backward*. This makes it less likely that victims will be kicked.

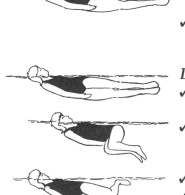

Body and Head Position. Technique is as follows:

✓ The trunk is stretched out on its back. The hips are turned so that the legs are on their side. The body is in a streamlined position, as horizontal as possible.

✓ The back of the head is cradled by the water in a position of maximum buoyancy.

Leg Action. Recovery in the leg action is as follows:

✓ Start the kick by bending at the hips and knees with the legs and feet together.

✓ Recover the legs together, and keep them in front of the trunk to reduce resistance. Keep the shins parallel to the body.

✓ Extend the top leg *backward*, with the toes pointed.

✓ Extend the bottom leg *forward* with the ankle flexed (toes drawn up toward the shin) until the legs are straight.

Technique for the drive is as follows:

✓ Drive the legs backward. Water pressure is felt against the sole of the bottom foot and the upper surface of the top foot.
✓ Kick continuously, trying not to pause.

Breathing. Inhale during the recovery, and exhale during the drive.

Sculling and Finning

Lifesavers use sculling and finning for movement and support (for example, the ready position in rescues).

Ready position

Body and Head Position

✓ Lie on your back, with your arms relaxed at your sides.
✓ Cradle the head on the water in line with the body.

Sculling, side view

Sculling Arm Action

✓ Hold the hands bent at about 45°, with the palms always facing *opposite* the line of travel and the elbows bent the way they would be if your hands were on your hips.
✓ Lift the little-finger sides of the hands to about 45°. Sweep the palms outward to a point where the elbows are almost straight. The drive comes from the palms pushing the water.
✓ Quickly tilt the hands so that the thumb sides are lifted to about 45°. Drive the hands inward to the body again.
✓ Scull with the wrist and fingertips in the same plane — it helps you stay in one place.
✓ To travel, change the angle of the wrist:
  ● fingers up to travel head-first
  ● fingers down to travel feet-first.

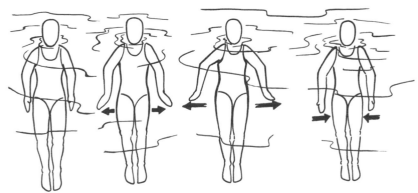

Sculling, overhead view

Finning Arm Action

Technique for the recovery is as follows:

✓ The elbow flexes, and the hands are drawn along the body to the waist.

✓ Fingers first and just below the surface, the hands move away from the body. They bring the forearm to about 90° to the body, wrist extended and palms facing the feet.

The key points for the drive are as follows:

✓ Without pausing, the elbows and wrists are vigorously extended. The palm pushes through to the thigh.

✓ A short glide precedes the next recovery.

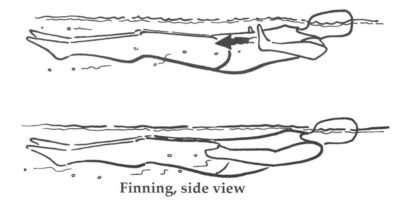

Finning, side view

Surface Dives

Surface dives enable rescuers to move quickly and efficiently from the surface to the desired depth underwater. To start an underwater swim for a search, victim recovery, or rescue approach, you need to be able to do surface dives.

Foot-first Surface Dive

When you do not know the water or the area might have underwater hazards, you should do a foot-first surface dive:

✓ From a swimming position, raise the head and tuck the knees toward the chest to stop forward motion and to rotate into an upright position.

✓ Press the arms vigorously downward to the thigh. At the same time, give a vigorous whip or scissor kick with the legs. These actions raise the trunk out of the water, which eases the descent phase.

✓ At the highest point in the ascent, take a breath. The body is streamlined, the arms at the sides, the legs straight and together, and the feet pointed to the bottom.

✓ You sink. When the head is below the surface, rotate the hands so that the palms are turned *out* and *up*.

✓ With the elbows bent, push vigorously up. Keep the legs extended in a streamlined position. These actions aid the descent.

> When practising surface dives, you need to understand the dangers of hyperventilation. See page 17 of this chapter.

> When you use this dive as a defence, do NOT raise the trunk out of the water before submerging. A victim could easily grab you.

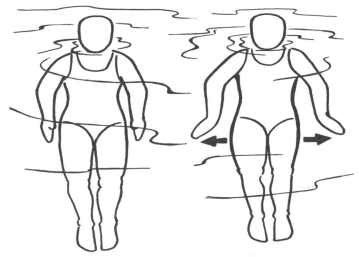

✓ Various techniques can be used to *get into* the underwater swim from a foot-first surface dive. One way is to tuck the knees toward the chest and extend the arms and head forward. Another way is to arch the back during the descent and bend the legs at the knees. This produces a levelling action at the desired depth, with the action depending on the amount of arch and knee bend.

Head-first Surface Dive

You can do head-first surface dives using a *pike* or a *tuck* position. Most surface dives are preceded by head-up swimming.

Using a Pike Position. Technique using a pike position is as follows:

✓ From a position of full extension in the breaststroke or front crawl, start the arm pull, take a breath, and pull down into a pike position. When swimming front crawl, use a one-arm pull *down* to start.

✓ The head and shoulders are now completely submerged. Hold the legs extended and streamlined.

✓ Rotate the arms and wrists so that the palms face downward. Pull the arms vigorously down and forward so that they extend toward the bottom.

✓ The extended legs lift, partly because of the arm movement and partly because of the work the abdominal muscles and back do to extend the legs. The body is fully extended, directed toward the bottom at about 15° from the vertical. The legs are mainly above the surface.

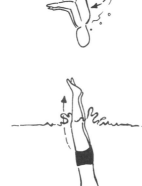

✓ The weight of the legs pushes you below the surface.
✓ To level off underwater, raise the head and arms while arching the back slightly. The underwater swim may now begin.

Using a Tuck Position. Technique using a tuck position is as follows:
✓ The arm action is identical to that for dives from a pike position (see above).
✓ During the forward arm thrust, tuck the legs by drawing the knees toward the chest. This action makes it easier to rotate into the head-downward position.
✓ Once the head and arms are streamlined, extend the hips, knees, and ankles suddenly and straight up. This action makes the body descend rapidly.

> ### Safety in Surface Dives
> ❑ Use foot-first dives in unknown water.
> ❑ Use head-first dives only in clear, deep water.
> ❑ Dive with a partner.
>
> ### Descent
> ❑ Your ears may hurt while descending. You can relieve the pain by closing your mouth, holding your nose, and gently blowing.
> ❑ If your ears still hurt, return to the surface, and do not keep diving.
>
> ### Ascent
> ❑ Ascend slowly. Follow your bubbles to the surface.
> ❑ DON'T HOLD YOUR BREATH! Exhale slowly while ascending.
> ❑ Rotate through 360° when searching in unknown water — it helps you see hazards more effectively.
> ❑ Extend an arm above your head, and look up!

> In the dolphin kick, the legs move together, with the knees and hips flexing and then extending in the drive phase. The leg action is slow and relaxed.

Underwater Swimming

To perform underwater searches or recover victims underwater, you need to be able to swim well underwater. One of the most efficient techniques for such swimming is a modified breaststroke. An alternating whip kick and dolphin kick is also very propulsive.

Body Position
✓ Start in a position of full extension, with the arms stretched in front of and below the head.

Arm Action
Drive. Drive in the arm action is as follows:
✓ Flex the wrists and elbows as the arms are pulled backward and upward. When the arms pass a 90° angle to the trunk, draw the elbows in to the sides.

✓ The wrists are hyperextended and the elbows extended as the arms push through to the thigh. Throughout this pull, the palms are nearly vertical and face backward. At the end of the pull, the hands are streamlined at the thighs, with the palms facing upward.
✓ If the water is not clear, one arm should be extended and held at the side of the head. This will protect the head and face from injury and assist in victim search.

Recovery. Technique is as follows:
✓ Draw the hands forward under the body. Keep the forearms in line with the hands as the arms fully extend again in front of and below the head.

Leg Action
✓ Use a whip, scissor, or flutter kick.

Co-ordination
✓ If using a whip or scissor kick, hold the body streamlined following the arm pull.
✓ Recover the legs as the arms recover.
✓ Drive with the legs as you bring the arms to full extension.
✓ Drive with the arms right after finishing the kick. While the arm pull is occurring, do a vigorous dolphin kick.
✓ A pause or glide can be very effective if you have a powerful whip kick.

To control depth, you may
✓ raise or lower your head
✓ arch or flex at the waist
✓ push downward at the start of the arm pull
✓ pull upward at the end of the drive phase of the arm action.

Hyperventilation

When practising underwater swims, many people want to increase the time they can stay submerged and the distances they can swim. They often try taking a series of deep breaths in which they quickly inhale and exhale fully. This overbreathing is called *hyperventilation*, and it is dangerous.

Hyperventilation does not increase the oxygen level in the body much, and so it does not provide any advantage to the swimmer. It does, however, greatly decrease the level of carbon dioxide in the body. This is dangerous, because the carbon-dioxide level causes the brain to signal the body to breathe.

When overbreathing is followed by exercise, oxygen is used up, and the carbon-dioxide level is slow to rise. The oxygen level may drop so far that the swimmer loses consciousness before feeling the need to take a breath.

The swimmer's loss of consciousness may be hard to detect, as he or she may swim for a few seconds afterward. Or the swimmer may surface when close to losing consciousness — but lack the strength to lift the head to breathe.

Know the dangers of hyperventilation, and *avoid* it!

9.4   Want to Know More?

Paul, Marianne. *Instructor Notes*. Ottawa: Royal Life Saving Society Canada, 1987.

> This manual is for Lifesaving Instructors and Examiners. It covers principles of learning, teaching, and evaluating lifesaving knowledge, skill, rescue, and fitness.

Swimming/Natation Canada. *Coaching Young Swimmers*. Gloucester: Swimming/Natation Canada, 1990.

> This manual is designed mainly for coaches of swimmers 12 and under, and it focuses on the technical aspects of competitive swimming. There are 19 chapters, with 6 on strokes, starts, and turns. Each of these technical chapters includes a teaching progression and charts on error detection and correction.

Swimming/Natation Canada. *The Esso Swim Canada Instructor Manual*. Gloucester: Swimming/Natation Canada, 1982.

> This manual is for instructors in Esso Swim Canada's skill-development program. The manual describes how to teach and evaluate the basic skills of modern competitive swimming.

Chapter 10
Physical Fitness and Lifesaving

10.1   Introduction

Thousands of articles and books have been written about physical fitness. Researchers have found that fitness reduces the risk of many diseases, helps people feel better and work more effectively, and increases people's overall sense of well-being.

But why is physical fitness important to you as a lifesaver? Because you *need* fitness in rescues. It plays a major role in how effectively you perform physical skills in a rescue. It also helps you make the most of your *mental* skills. For example, your fitness strongly affects how well you make judgments, reach decisions, and deal with stress in a rescue. Performing positively as a lifesaver thus requires both the "physical" and "mental" sides of fitness.

This chapter provides an *overview* of physical fitness. It stresses the role of fitness in lifesaving, and it presents tips on how to develop and maintain fitness. This information should help you make any needed adjustments in your fitness training. The following aspects of fitness are covered:
❑ the benefits of physical fitness
❑ the components of physical fitness
❑ evaluating, developing, and maintaining physical fitness.

10.2   Benefits of Physical Fitness

Physical fitness is the ability to do what you want or need to do *without getting too tired*. For instance, you can play basketball or run for a bus without feeling exhausted. You can lifeguard after classes and feel energetic while on duty. You can even stay up later than you should to study — and feel fresh and alert the next day. In a word, being physically fit makes things *easier*.

> Physical fitness is about a lot more than being strong or thin. And fitness isn't something you *have* — it's a *process*, or something you *do*.

As the introduction to this chapter pointed out, fitness has both *physical* and *mental* benefits. Here are just some of the physical benefits:
✓ better performance of physical skills
✓ lower risk of muscle injury
✓ faster and better healing from injuries that *do* occur
✓ improved blood circulation
✓ improved cardiovascular ("heart and lung") fitness, including lower risk of heart attack or stroke
✓ better body composition (see page 10-3)
✓ decreased risk of osteoporosis (thinning of bones).

> ### Physical Activity, Exercise, and Active Living
> Physical fitness is *related* to some terms you've probably heard many times: physical activity, exercise, and active living. But how is it different from them?
>
> Physical activity refers to all the movements you make in your daily activities. Recreational activities are part of physical activity, and so are work-related activities. Even *sleep* is a physical activity!
>
> Exercise is *part* of physical activity, but it isn't the *same* as physical activity. Exercise is physical activity that is planned, structured, and repetitive — swimming three times a week, for example. Exercise also has a *purpose*: improving or maintaining physical fitness.
>
> Active living is an *approach* to physical activity. Active living means making physical activity *part of your life*. For instance, walking to school instead of taking the bus is active living, and so is taking the stairs instead of the elevator when you go to an office building.

The mental benefits include
✓ better mental functioning
✓ better self-concept and higher self-esteem
✓ less anxiety and depression
✓ greater capacity to cope with stress.

10.3   Components of Physical Fitness

When experts talk about physical fitness, they divide it into five components. Each of these components plays an important role in lifesaving:
❑ body composition
❑ flexibility
❑ muscular strength
❑ muscular endurance
❑ aerobic fitness.

The rest of this section defines the five components of fitness. Section 10.4 then describes how to evaluate, develop, and maintain each component.

 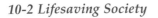

Body Composition

Body composition refers to how your body is made up: for example, the amount of fat compared with the amount of muscle in your body or your height relative to your weight. There are three basic *body types*:

❑ ectomorphs — bodies with light frames, low percentage of body fat, and long, thin, muscles

❑ mesomorphs — bodies with medium frames, medium percentage of body fat, and well-developed muscles

❑ endomorphs — bodies with heavy frames, higher percentage of body fat, and a higher capacity for good muscular development.

Everyone is born with a certain body type. Because of this, there are aspects of our body composition we CANNOT control. But we can all get the right *balance* of fat and muscle for our type.

The body mass index (BMI) is a widely accepted measure of this balance. To find out what your BMI is, use the equation BMI = body weight (in kilograms) ÷ height^2 (in metres). For example, if you weigh 64 kilograms and are 1.7 metres tall, your BMI is 22 ($64 ÷ 1.7^2 = 22$).

For those aged 15 to 19, a BMI of less than 19 or more than 24 is believed to represent a health risk. It is recommended that you consult your physician or a nutritionist if your BMI is less than 19 or more than 24.

Flexibility

Flexibility refers to your ability to move easily within your normal range of motion. If you have good flexibility, you can — if necessary — move to the very end of this range of motion without pain or injury.

Back and leg flexibility are needed for reaching assists

Flexibility is specific to each joint in your body. The flexibility of your muscles, ligaments, and tendons determines the amount of movement at each joint.

In lifesaving, you need flexibility in your back and legs to do such things as foot-first surface dives or dive entries.

Muscular Strength

Muscular strength refers to the peak force produced by a particular muscle group in a one-time effort (single contraction). This strength does *not* refer to overall body strength.

In lifesaving, you need muscular strength to do removals.

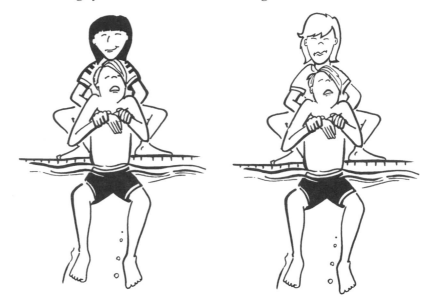

Muscular strength is needed for removals

Muscular Endurance

Muscular endurance refers to your muscles' ability to keep producing force for a moderate amount of time.

In lifesaving, you need muscular endurance in head-up approaches and endurance swims.

Muscular endurance is needed for approaches

Aerobic Fitness

Aerobic fitness refers to your body's ability to perform tasks for an extended period of time. This kind of fitness is also called *cardiorespiratory fitness* or *cardiovascular fitness*. Aerobic fitness is often described as the most important component of fitness.

The greater your aerobic fitness, the longer you can work at a given level of intensity.

In lifesaving, aerobic fitness is needed in underwater swims and endurance swims.

10.4 Evaluating, Developing, and Maintaining Physical Fitness

As a lifesaver, you need to develop and maintain *all five components* of physical fitness (see Section 10.3 for information on the role each plays in lifesaving). The first step in this process is to find out where you are *now*. In other words, you need to *evaluate* the five components.

The chart on pages 10-8 and 10-9 shows how to do this for all five components of fitness. Here are some tips on using this chart:

✓ First, evaluate where you are on each component. If you feel you need to take specific tests, consult a certified fitness appraiser (see page 10-9).

✓ *Before you start any new activity*, ask yourself if there's any health reason for you *not* to do it. If you have any doubts at all, you may want to consult your doctor.

✓ Next, decide *how* to develop and maintain each component. When you're making this decision, choose activities and locations *you* enjoy — it'll keep you motivated.

✓ Start from where you are *now*. For example, use your current level of participation as a base. This is much better for your health than suddenly and dramatically increasing your activity level. But it'll also motivate you, because setting unrealistic goals can discourage you if you don't reach them.

✓ Exercise at a *moderate* level of intensity. Make sure you can pass the "talk test" — talk at your normal volume and pace, without gasping — while you exercise. If you can't do this, you could be working your heart and lungs too much.

✓ Increase your activity *gradually* — it reduces the risk of injury, and it'll keep you motivated.

✓ Watch out for signs you're doing too much. Feeling fatigue in your muscles is normal. But *some* muscle aches indicate overtraining or potential injury. *Any* sharp pain in your muscles or joints is a sign the activity isn't appropriate.

> **Choose Activities and Locations You Enjoy**
> ✓ Do land or water activities — or both!!
> ✓ If you like to exercise alone, consider swimming, walking, cycling, or running. Or do exercises at home, perhaps with exercise videos. You might even do weight training at home.
> ✓ If you like exercising with others, find classes, clubs, or teams that interest you.
> ✓ If you prefer team activity, how about tennis, basketball, volleyball, or water polo?
> ✓ Remember that there are as many ways to develop fitness as there are people. The possibilities are endless — just use your creativity!

Make sure you can pass the "talk test"

✓ Vary the activities you do — it makes things more interesting, keeps you more motivated, and increases the chances of all-round development.

✓ If you want to, keep *track* of your fitness progress — that way, you can *see* your progress. A chart like that below is just one of the ways you can record your progress on all five components of fitness.

✓ Enjoy!!

Choose activities you enjoy

My Personal Fitness Goals and Gains								
Component of Fitness	**My Goals for _____** (date)		**My Goals for _____** (date)		**My Goals for _____** (date)		**My Goals for _____** (date)	
	Goal	*Gains*	*Goal*	*Gains*	*Goal*	*Gains*	*Goal*	*Gains*
Body Composition								
Flexibility								
Muscular Strength								
Muscular Endurance								
Aerobic Fitness								

Heart Rate and Training Zone

Taking your pulse (heart rate) tells you *directly* how hard your heart is working. During aerobic exercise, your heart rate should be in the so-called *training zone*. Your heart rate should fall to its resting rate within a few minutes of stopping exercising. Here is some basic information on heart rates and training zones.

Taking Your Heart Rate

Taking your heart rate involves feeling your pulse and counting the number of beats. You can take your pulse at the *carotid* or *radial* artery (see illustrations, page 6-5). To take your pulse at the carotid artery,

✓ put the thumb of one hand on your chin
✓ place the middle three fingers of the same hand on the side of the neck, just below and in front of the jaw
✓ press just hard enough to feel the pulse
✓ with the first beat counting as zero, count the number of beats in 10 seconds.

To take your pulse at the radial artery,
✓ place the middle three fingers of one hand along the edge of the wrist at the base of the thumb
✓ press just hard enough to feel the pulse
✓ with the first beat counting as zero, count the number of beats in 10 seconds.

Being in Your Training Zone

✓ Refer to the chart below to find the *training zone*. The training zone is the range your heart rate needs to be in for you to benefit aerobically from physical activity.
✓ Find your pulse, and determine your heart rate (number of beats) for 10 seconds.
✓ Look along the bottom axis, find your age, and locate your heart rate on the chart. Are you within the training zone?
✓ If your heart rate is below this zone, you won't benefit enough from your training. And if your heart rate is above this zone, you're probably working too hard.

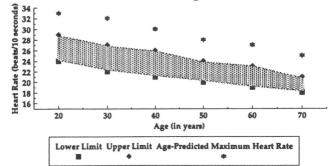

Heart Rate Training Zone

A Word of Caution

The heart rates presented in the training-zone chart are *guidelines*. There are no absolutes in this area, and many factors go into determining your training zone:

❏ There is great individual variation in resting and exercise heart rates. Two equally fit people can have different resting and exercise heart rates. By knowing and keeping track of *your* heart rate, you can apply the chart to yourself.
❏ Many factors can raise or lower your heart rate. For example, being tired or sick can affect it. So can gaining weight or exercising in difficult weather conditions (heat and humidity, for instance). Be sure to take this into account when you use the chart.
❏ The chart refers to exercise on land. There is evidence that exercising in the water results in a *lower* heart rate than exercising at the same intensity on land. Some research suggests this difference in heart rates is about 10%. While this research is still inconclusive, you need to account for the *existence* of this difference when using the chart for aquatic exercise.

How to Develop and Maintain Physical Fitness

Component	How to Evaluate This Component	How to Develop and Maintain This Component
Body Composition [the amount of fat compared with the amount of muscle in your body]	✓ Use the body mass index equation, on page 10-3.	✓ *All* physical activity can improve body composition. ✓ A healthy diet, as outlined in *Canada's Food Guide to Healthy Eating*, can also improve this component.

Flexibility [the ability to move easily within your normal range of motion]	✓ To evaluate your *general* flexibility, do the long sitting test.[1] It tests the flexibility of the shoulders, back, thighs, and the backs of the legs.
	✓ For a more *specific* evaluation, move an individual joint to the end of its range of motion, and *feel* the volume and intensity of the muscle's resistance.
	✓ After working on your flexibility for a few weeks, see if you can stretch farther. If you can, your flexibility has improved.
		✓ Stretching will improve your flexibility and decrease the risk of injury. (See page 10-10 for illustrations of stretching exercises.)
		✓ Stretch slowly and steadily, and hold each stretch for 5 to 10 seconds.
		✓ DON'T bounce — it can cause injuries.
		✓ Stretch each muscle group 3 to 5 times *before* activity. For example,
		  ● do shoulder and gluteal stretches before removals
		  ● do back and leg stretches before dives, surface dives, or front-roll entries
		  ● do arm and leg stretches before endurance swims.

Muscular Strength [the peak force produced by a muscle group in a one-time effort]	✓ Using principles of safe lifting (see page 4-24), do a maximal one-time lift. Start with no weight, increase to a low weight, and *then* try a maximal weight.
	✓ You can also evaluate muscular strength in the upper body. To do this, place weigh scales on a counter or table (above the waist). Push down on the scale with your hands, and read the number.
		✓ Practise safe movements in *all* lifting (see page 4-24).
		✓ Do 3 to 5 repetitions *at mild to moderate intensity*. Rest enough between repetitions that you can do the activity again at the original level of resistance. For instance,
		  ● lift a weight from the bottom of the pool 3 to 5 times
		  ● do 3 to 5 removals
		  ● tread water for 1 minute 3 to 5 times
		  ● do 3 to 5 push-ups at the side of the pool.
		
		Note: Intensity is *specific to the individual*, and it is affected by your age, size, and skill level.

How to Develop and Maintain Physical Fitness (cont'd)

Component	How to Evaluate This Component	How to Develop and Maintain This Component
Muscular Endurance [the ability to keep producing force for a moderate amount of time]	✓ Do as many repetitions of an activity as you can in 1 to 2 minutes. ✓ Push-ups, chin-ups, and sit-ups can all be used to test muscular endurance, as can the number of pool-side pull-ups you can do in 1 minute.	✓ Do 5 to 10 repetitions *at mild to moderate intensity*. Rest enough between repetitions that you can do the activity again at the original level of resistance. For instance, ● tread water for 1 minute 5 to 10 times ● swim 5 lengths of the pool 5 times ● do 5 to 10 removals ● do 5 to 10 pull-ups from the side of the pool. **Note:** Intensity is *specific to the individual*, and it is affected by your age, size, and skill level.
Aerobic Fitness [the ability to perform tasks for an extended period of time]	✓ Take the Canadian Standardized Test of Fitness (see page 10-11) from a certified fitness appraiser[2] or other fitness tests as recommended by your local recreation centre. ✓ Step tests and treadmill tests should be conducted and administered by certified fitness appraisers.	✓ To improve your aerobic fitness, you need to do 15 to 20 minutes of exercise three times a week with your heart rate in its training zone (see page 10-7). ✓ Swimming, cycling, walking, running, and dancing are all aerobic activities.

Notes:
1. For the long sitting test (see page 10-10), measure the number of centimetres between the fingers and foot placement. A negative score is obtained if the fingertips do not reach the foot placement, and a positive score is obtained if the fingertips reach beyond the feet.
2. If you feel you need to take specific tests for any component, consult a certified fitness appraiser. Local pools, recreation centres, YMCA-YWCAs, and many fitness centres have such appraisers on staff.

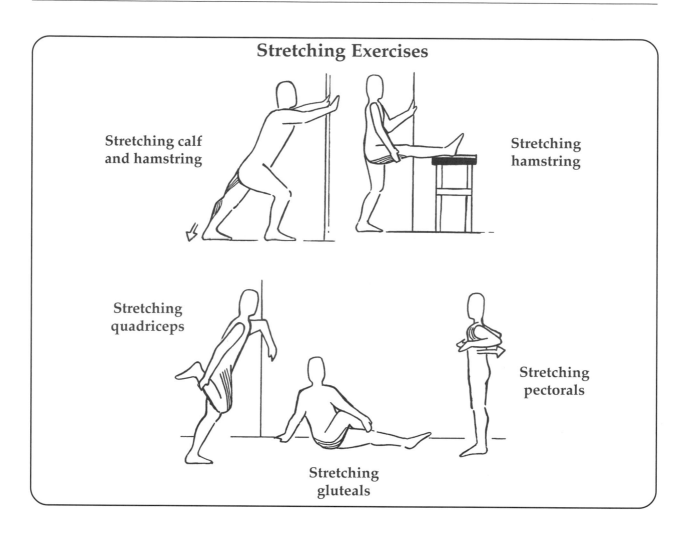

Stretching Exercises

Stretching calf
and hamstring

Stretching
hamstring

Stretching
quadriceps

Stretching
pectorals

Stretching
gluteals

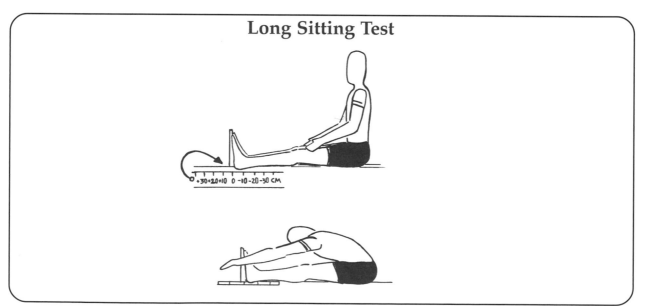

Long Sitting Test

+30 +20 +10   0 -10 -20 -30 CM

10.5   Want to Know More?

Caspersen, C. J. , K. E. Powell, and G. M. Christenson. "Physical Activity, Exercise and Physical Fitness," *Public Health Reports* 100:126-131, 1985.
>   This is an advanced article that reviews different definitions and descriptions of physical fitness used in studies on fitness. The authors are widely respected experts, and the article is considered a classic.

Fitness and Amateur Sport Canada. *Canadian Standardized Test of Fitness*, third edition. Ottawa: Fitness and Amateur Sport, 1986.
>   *Canadian Standardized Test of Fitness (CSTF)* is a set of procedures that can be used to evaluate specific components of fitness, including cardiovascular fitness. *CSTF* is designed mainly for fitness appraisers, and its purpose is to provide simple, safe, and practical procedures for evaluating fitness.

Nieman, David C. *The Sports Medicine Fitness Course*. Palo Alto, California: Bull Publishing, 1986.
>   This is a comprehensive textbook (455 pages) covering fitness principles and assessment techniques.

Ontario, Ministry of Health. *Healthy Weights*. Toronto: Ministry of Health, 1991.
>   The purpose of this 14-page booklet is to help people set and achieve weight goals that are realistic and healthy. The booklet explains why strict diets *don't* work and describes an outlook on eating and exercise that will help people achieve and maintain a healthy weight. Included in the booklet are weight guidelines, a summary of Canada's Food Guide, and suggestions for getting on the right track regarding eating habits.

Appendix A
Stress Reactions to Rescues

Rescuers can have strong reactions to emergencies. These reactions may be physical, mental, or emotional. When these reactions interfere with the ability to function during or after the emergency, they are referred to as *critical incident stress syndrome*.

Many things can cause critical incident stress syndrome. Here are just a few examples:
- ❑ rescuing and treating a victim who was injured or died
- ❑ knowing the victim or having the victim resemble someone you know
- ❑ being involved in an incident that got a lot of media attention
- ❑ being involved in a threatening situation, such as one with severe water or weather conditions
- ❑ being involved in an incident when rescuers had to decide which victims got priority for treatment.

Here are some of the signs and symptoms of *acute* critical incident stress syndrome.

Signs and Symptoms of Acute Critical Incident Stress Syndrome		
Physical	*Mental*	*Emotional*
❑ Nausea, sweating, tremors ❑ Disorientation, loss of co-ordination ❑ Increase in heart rate and blood pressure ❑ Hyperventilation, with chest pains and headaches ❑ Muscle soreness ❑ Difficulty sleeping, fatigue	❑ Impaired thinking and decision making ❑ Poor concentration, confusion, difficulty performing simple mental tasks ❑ Difficulty with tasks involving the memory ❑ Flashbacks	❑ Anxiety, fear, guilt ❑ Grief, depression ❑ Emotional numbness ❑ Feeling lost, abandoned, helpless ❑ Withdrawal from others ❑ Anger, resentment, scapegoating ❑ Feeling overwhelmed

Signs and symptoms of *delayed* critical incident stress syndrome include

❑ increasing feelings of depression, anxiety, and irritability
❑ sleep disturbance
❑ changes in eating habits
❑ loss of emotional control
❑ feelings of isolation
❑ disturbances of the menstrual cycle
❑ increased problems with interpersonal relations
❑ disturbing memories
❑ fear of repetition of the incident.

You need to be aware of the reactions associated with critical incident stress syndrome. It is also important to *deal with* such stress. Debriefing meetings, group discussions, team meetings, peer counselling, and professional counselling are all useful ways to cope with and relieve the stress reaction. Here are some tips on what to do and what NOT to do after a critical incident.

After a Critical Incident: Some Do's and Don'ts	
Do	*Don't*
✓ Expect the incident to bother you	✗ Deny your reactions, for example, by drinking or taking drugs
✓ Follow a good diet	✗ Withdraw from family, friends, and co-workers
✓ Exercise	✗ Automatically avoid work
✓ Take time for leisure activities	✗ Use off-duty time for training immediately after the incident
✓ Remind yourself that your reactions are normal	✗ Look for easy answers to explain why the incident happened
✓ Learn as much as you can about critical incident stress syndrome	✗ Think you're crazy
✓ Spend time with family, friends, and co-workers	✗ Have unrealistic expectations for recovery
✓ Find someone you're comfortable with, and share your feelings about the incident with him or her	
✓ Realize that it can take *months* or *years* to deal with all aspects of an incident	
✓ Get extra help if necessary	

Appendix B
The Society's Policy Guidelines on Rescue Breathing Practice

The Royal Life Saving Society Canada acknowledges its responsibility to inform participants of possible cross-contamination resulting from rescue breathing practice.

Medical evidence suggests that cross-contamination may result from mouth-to-mouth, hand-to-mouth, hand-to-eye, or hand-to-nose contact. Diseases that may be transmitted in this manner include infectious mononucleosis, hepatitis A (infectious hepatitis), hepatitis B (serum hepatitis), herpes simplex, the common cold (rhinovirus), and tuberculosis.

There is no evidence that acquired immune deficiency syndrome (AIDS) can be transmitted by mouth-to-mouth contact.

The Society does not require direct contact with another person in rescue breathing to achieve a Society award. Instructors and Examiners should respect candidates' preference to demonstrate rescue breathing with a partner of their choice (with or without direct contact) or manikin or suitable device.

When a partner is selected, candidates demonstrate all steps in rescue breathing (including airway management) up to the point of contact. The evaluator should question the candidate to ensure that he or she understands the reasons for, and methods of, effectively sealing the mouth and nose and inflating the victim's lungs.

When manikins are used, candidates demonstrate all the procedures for rescue breathing including an effective seal of the mouth or nose and ability to inflate the victim's lungs. To minimize the risk of transferring an infection between participants, minimize the number of individuals using the same manikin. After each candidate uses it, the manikin should be effectively cleaned according to acceptable medical procedures. (For detailed cleaning instructions, see page 7-16.)

When a device is selected, it should allow the candidate to demonstrate correct seal and inflation.

To minimize the risk of transferring an infection, individuals with known transmittable diseases or with obvious infections (e.g., colds, cold sores, coughs, or respiratory infections) should not participate in rescue breathing practice.

Appendix C
Swimming Principles

Introduction

To develop efficient strokes, you need to apply certain *swimming principles*. These principles are about what happens in water:

❑ flotation — what makes you float or sink
❑ propulsion — what makes you move
❑ resistance — what holds you back
❑ levers — what helps you move loads.

This appendix describes each of the four principles and includes experiments you can do to learn about these principles first-hand. It also describes how to apply each principle i
 swimming.

Flotation Principles

The principle of *flotation* is about what makes you float or sink in water. Flotation is affected by

❑ water pressure
❑ water displacement
❑ density
❑ specific gravity
❑ body type
❑ balance.

Water Pressure

Water exerts *pressure* equally in all directions on anything submerged in it. This pressure increases with the depth of the water. While the water's pressure is equal on the sides of the body, water pressure *under* the body is greater than that *above* it, because the bottom of the body is deeper. The result is an upward force, called *buoyancy* or *buoyant force*. The larger a body is, the greater its buoyant force. "Effective" buoyancy occurs whenever the weight of a body in water is less than the weight of the water it displaces.

> **Try This! Water Pressure**
> To see how water exerts pressure that increases with depth,
> ❑ take an inflated balloon to the bottom of a pool or lake. What happens to it?
> ❑ try it again, but surface slowly this time. What happens to the balloon as you get closer to the surface?

Try This! Density
Float in the most relaxed position you can:
- ❏ Try it with your lungs full of air. How well do you float?
- ❏ Blow air out slowly. What happens?

Many people sink when they breathe out or lift a limb out of the water. This happens because they have *increased* their density. Their mass has stayed the same, but they have *lowered* the volume of water they displace.

Water Displacement

Large bodies *displace*, or move, large amounts of water. The weight of the displaced water seems to be "taken away" from the weight of bodies in water. Bodies float if the weight of water they displace is greater than their own weight.

Density

A body's *volume* (or size) affects whether the body will float. The ratio of a body's mass to its volume is called its *density*. Density equals mass divided by volume:

Density = Mass/Volume.

Objects with a high density, such as those made of metal, tend to sink. Objects with a low density, such as cork or wood, tend to float.

Specific Gravity

Buoyancy is often measured in terms of *specific gravity*. The specific gravity of a body is its weight divided by the weight of the water it displaces when completely submerged:

Specific gravity = Weight of body/Weight of water displaced.

Here are some facts about specific gravity:
- ❏ A body will float in water if the water it displaces when completely submerged weighs *more* than it does (specific gravity is less than 1).
- ❏ A body will sink in water if the water it displaces weighs *less* than it does (specific gravity is greater than 1).
- ❏ A submerged body will stay in the same position (neither floating nor sinking) if the water it displaces weighs *the same* as it does (specific gravity equals 1).

Body Type

The human body contains muscle, bone, and fat. The specific gravity of muscle and bone is greater than 1. The specific gravity of fat is less than 1. This is how *body type* affects whether you float:
- ❏ People with a high percentage of body fat (endomorphs) usually have a specific gravity less than 1. So they tend to float.
- ❏ People with a low percentage of body fat and light bone density (ectomorphs) usually have a specific gravity less than 1. They tend to float.

Try This! Water Displacement
Run a few inches of water in the bathtub. What happens to the water level when you sit down in the tub? Is the effect different if you sit in different positions:
- ❏ with your legs extended?
- ❏ with your knees bent?

❑ People with heavy bone density or a high percentage of muscle tissue (mesomorphs) usually have a specific gravity greater than 1. They therefore tend to sink.

Balance

People keep their *balance* on land by maintaining support under their *centre of gravity*. This is the point in the body around which its mass is evenly balanced. When the body *isn't* supported at this point, the body moves until the centre of gravity is as low as possible. For example, if you lean over too far, you'll fall to the ground!

Swimmers must also keep their balance in water. They can do this by keeping their centre of gravity directly below their *centre of buoyancy* (which is near the lungs).

> **Try This! Balance**
> Try floating in different positions *without moving:*
> ❑ Try to float on your back with your arms at your sides. Can you hold your position without sinking?
> ❑ Try floating on your back with your arms extended in the water above your head. Is it easier or harder?
> ❑ Try floating vertically, with only your face out of the water. Does your body stay stable, or do you "lose your balance"?
> ❑ What other positions can you float in without moving?

Applying Flotation Principles

To apply flotation principles in swimming,
✓ keep as much of your body as possible in the water
✓ control your breathing — keep the lungs full to float, and breathe out to descend
✓ keep your muscles as relaxed as possible (don't tense up).

Propulsion Principles

The force that pushes you through the water is called *propulsion*.
Propulsion is affected by several aspects of motion:
❑ inertia
❑ acceleration
❑ action and reaction.

Inertia

The principle of *inertia* says that
❑ bodies at rest tend to stay at rest until acted upon by an outside force
❑ bodies in motion tend to stay in motion until acted upon by an outside force.

When you want to start swimming from a stationary position, *you* have to provide the force to overcome inertia. Once you're moving, water provides the force to stop you.

> **Try This! Inertia**
> ❑ Swim a pool-length of breaststroke. How many strokes did it take?
> ❑ Swim the same distance again, but let your body come to a complete stop between strokes. Did it take more or fewer strokes to cover the same distance?

Acceleration

Acceleration is an increase in speed. The principle of acceleration says that when a force is applied to a body, the body's acceleration
- ❏ increases as the force does
- ❏ is less for heavier bodies.

> **Try This! Acceleration**
> - ❏ Swim a length of the pool on your back, using only your legs and using a whip kick.
> - ❏ Next do 10 to 12 kicks where you bend the legs up at the same speed as you extend them down. What direction did you travel, compared with your first length?
> - ❏ Then do the same number of kicks as above, but bend the legs down slowly and extend them fast. Which direction did you go this time?

A force can make a body *accelerate* if it is applied in the same direction as the mass is moving. A force can make a body *decelerate* (decrease in speed) if it is applied in the direction opposite the one the mass is moving.

In breaststroke, for example, the legs kick hard rearward on the *drive* portion of the whip kick to get maximum forward movement. On the *recovery* portion of the kick, the legs move slowly to avoid pulling the body backward.

Action and Reaction

The principle of *action and reaction* says that every action has an equal and opposite reaction.

In swimming, this means you have to push against water in the direction *opposite* your line of travel. For example, to go forward, you push water backward. Any movements that push water up, down, or to the side use energy *without helping to move you forward*.

On a foot-first surface dive, for example, you make your arms pull and your legs kick toward the bottom to make the trunk come out of the water. Once the body submerges (because of the flotation principles discussed above), you push your arms toward the surface. The result is that you are forced toward the bottom.

> **Try This! Action and Reaction**
> Hold a pencil between your middle and ring fingers so that it is perpendicular to your fingers. Place the pencil so that the sharpened end points in the same direction as the palm of your hand.
>
> Try sculling on your back, still holding the pencil. First, try sculling with your hands flat, parallel to the water:
> - ❏ Where does the sharp end of the pencil point?
> - ❏ Are you travelling? If so, in which direction?
>
> Next, scull with your wrist bent so that your fingers point straight up:
> - ❏ Where does the pencil point now?
> - ❏ Are you travelling? Which direction?
>
> Next, scull with your wrist bent so that your fingers point straight down:
> - ❏ Where is the pencil pointing?
> - ❏ Are you travelling? Which direction?

Applying Propulsion Principles

To increase the forces that make you move,

✓ make propulsive actions as continuous as possible. Avoid long glides on breaststroke and during lifesaving kicks. Use continuous arm action on front crawl and back crawl.

✓ do the drive phase of strokes vigorously and the recovery phase slowly.

✓ apply forces in the direction *opposite* the one you want to go.

✓ don't apply forces in other directions.

✓ use the largest areas possible in propulsive actions. For instance, hold the palm of the hand flat, not cupped, during front and back crawl.

✓ use S-shaped pulls to pull "still" water. Water that isn't moving provides a stronger reaction to pulls and kicks than moving water. Use straight-line actions to pull against water that is already moving.

✓ pitch the hands at an angle of 30° to 45° to your path through the water. Besides giving good propulsion, this action gives some "lift," much as sculling does.

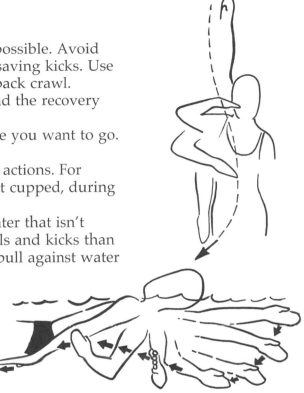

Resistance Principles

The force that holds you back in the water is called *resistance*. This is caused by water's density. While you can use resistance positively to move forward (action and reaction), negative resistance can force you to work harder.

The main types of resistance are
❑ frontal resistance
❑ eddy resistance.

Frontal Resistance

Frontal resistance is created by water "piling up" in front of you when you are swimming, the way snow piles up in front of a shovel or snowplough. Any part of the body that faces forward can create this resistance. The greater the body area exposed to the flow, the greater the resistance.

> **Try This! Resistance**
> Get a flutterboard or PFD, and swim some lengths of flutter kick or whip kick with it in different positions:
> ❑ Hold the flutterboard or PFD like a portrait, perpendicular to the water, with about 20 centimetres of it submerged.
> ❑ Hold the flutterboard or PFD like a landscape, again perpendicular to the water, with about 20 centimetres submerged.
>
> Try both of the above positions again, but this time try them with the flutterboard or PFD almost parallel to the water:
> ❑ In which position was it hardest to swim with the aid?
> ❑ In which position was it easiest?
> ❑ In which position was the biggest surface area of the aid pushing against the water?
> ❑ In which position was the least surface area pushing against the water?

Eddy Resistance

As a body moves through water, water flows around the body. The result is *eddy resistance*, or *drag*. Eddy resistance increases when you fishtail — move too much from side to side — rather than travel in a straight line. Streamlining the body reduces the effect of eddy drag.

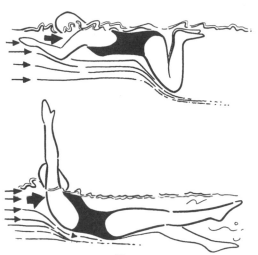

Poor streamlining

Cradling the head

Minimizing forces

Applying Resistance Principles

To lessen the effects of resistance,

✓ *streamline* your body. Make sure the submerged surface area facing the line of travel is as small as possible. For example, in front and back crawl, roll to both sides. Since the top shoulder is out of the water, this action reduces the resistance caused by the shoulders facing the line of travel.

Good streamlining

✓ use a body position as close to the horizontal as possible. (Some adjustments will be needed for whip kick.)

✓ don't submerge the head completely. Instead, let the water support it.

✓ travel in a straight line. (Keeping your eyes open will help you travel in a straight line.) Make sure you apply force in the right direction (opposite the line of travel). In addition, travel at constant speed throughout the distance being travelled.

Straight-line travel

✓ minimize the force of movements that oppose forward motion. For example, recover the legs slowly on the whip kick and drive them quickly and hard.

Lever Principles

Levers help you move loads that would otherwise be too heavy for you to move by yourself. Tools such as crowbars, corkscrews, and bottle openers are levers. Body parts are also levers.

Levers rotate around a point called a *fulcrum*. A force is applied at one point of the lever, turning around the fulcrum to move the load.

Levers help you most when the load is as close to the fulcrum as possible. You can increase the efficiency of the drive phase of most arm actions by keeping the load (where the fingers and arms feel or push against the water) close to the main fulcrum (the shoulder) and close to the body's centre line.

Applying Lever Principles

To apply lever principles in swimming, use bent-arm pulls on front and back crawl. For instance, in front crawl, use a bent-arm pull during the drive phase.

Bent-arm pull

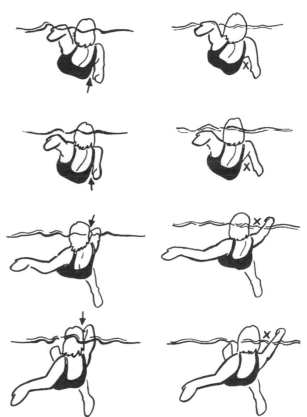

Efficient (left) and inefficient (right) arm action

> **Try This! Levers**
> Stand with your hands on the top of the back of a chair:
> ❏ Keeping your arms perfectly straight, lift the chair.
> ❏ Try lifting the chair again, but bend your elbows this time.
> ❏ Which time was the load (chair) closer to the fulcrum (your shoulder)?
> ❏ Which time was it easier to lift the chair?

Index